The official Londc
to all

LON
MUSEUMS

This book is your unique and authoritative guide to the wonders contained in all the museums in the capital. Indispensable to arts organisations and businesses, it is increasingly popular with teachers, tour guides and other group leaders. Libraries stock it, so do Tourist Information Centres – and now with this smaller format there is an edition to appeal to all Londoners and to visitors to our great city.

Since the last edition in 1990 times have become harsher. Recession hits museums too, though the rich variety revealed in these pages shows their continuing commitment to their role as repositories of our heritage. London's Museums are responding to the new atmosphere by offering better quality exhibitions and education programmes. Now is the time to check out what they have to offer you. You may be astonished!

London Transport Services

The Travel Information Service is London Transport's shop window. It exists to provide passengers and potential passengers with helpful advice and guidance about every aspect of travelling around London – by bus, by tube, by the Docklands Light Railway and by British Rail. It can also give general information about the London tourist scene. The locations of Travel Information Centres are given below. Alternatively, phone 071-222 1234.

Travel Information Centres

These are open at Underground stations, Heathrow Airport and West Croydon bus station as follows:

EUSTON (BR Concourse), KING'S CROSS, LIVERPOOL STREET, OXFORD CIRCUS, PICCADILLY CIRCUS, ST JAMES'S PARK, VICTORIA (BR Concourse - opposite Platform 8), HEATHROW 1, 2, 3 (station), HEATHROW Terminals 1, 2, 3, 4, WEST CROYDON BUS STATION.

Published jointly by London Transport, 55 Broadway, Westminster, London SW1 and Book Production Consultants, 25-27 High Street, Chesterton, Cambridge CB4 1ND.

© London Museums Service
1993 (5th edition)
ISBN 1 871829 12 7

Editors
Judi Caton, Anne Robson

London Museums Service
Ferroners House
Barbican
London EC2Y 8AA

Cover design by Lawrence & Beavan
Design by Phil Kay Design
Produced by Book Production Consultants, Cambridge
Printed and bound by The Burlington Press, Foxton, Cambridge

Front Cover: London Transport Museum, British Museum
Title page: London Toy and Model Museum, British Museum

London Canal Museum

The London Museums Service is the London Regional Office of the Area Museums Service for South Eastern England (AMSSEE). Its purpose is to improve the quality and effectiveness of local and regional museum and gallery provision throughout Greater London, and in 1993 it celebrates its 10th birthday.

FUNDED BY

LONDON BOROUGHS GRANTS COMMITTEE

AMSSEE
Museums and Galleries Commission

CONTENTS

MUSEUMS IN LONDON

Entries are based on information provided by the museums themselves and are correct at the time of going to press. If you have special needs or intend visiting one of the smaller museums we recommend confirming opening hours and facilities with the museum itself to ensure a successful visit.

NEW PROJECTS IN LONDON

Museum projects in the process of development. Some are already open to visitors by appointment.

MUSEUMS BY BOROUGH

Useful listing of all the museums and projects in each borough.

MUSEUMS BY SUBJECT

A guide to the larger or more significant collections in each category.

USEFUL ADDRESSES

Exhibition and heritage venues, libraries and archives, professional and museum related bodies.

The National Gallery and Sainsbury Wing

THE SYMBOLS

£   Admission charges (based on one full paying adult)
     Free
+   £1.50 or less
++   £1.50 – £3.50
+++ Greater than £3.50
     Concessions
Ⓥ   Vending machine
🍷   Light refreshments available
✗   More substantial snacks or meals
🅿   Parking available
⊖   Tube station
⇌   British Rail station
🚌   Bus route numbers

Disabled Access Codes
Provided by ARTSLINE
☎ 071-388 2227, the free telephone information service on the arts in Greater London for people with disabilities. Telephone ARTSLINE or the museum itself to check on specific access conditions.

W   Museum with unstepped access via main or sidedoor, wheelchair spaces and adapted toilet
X   Museum with flat or one-stepped access to exhibition area
A   Museum with 2-5 steps to exhibition area
S   Museum with many unavoidable steps and/or other obstacles for wheelchair users
G   Provision made for guide dogs
E   Hearing loop system installed. Check with museum whether in operation

Alfred Dunhill Collection

30 Duke Street
St James's
London SW1Y 6DL
☎ 071-495 2023 Curator

Collection of antique pipes of all nations can be seen in the Duke Street shop during opening hours (09.30-17.30 Mon-Fri, 09.30-17.00 Sat). At 60/61 Burlington Arcade a collection of antique Dunhill motoring accessories, lighters, watches and pens can be viewed by appointment.

£ Free
X G
⊖ Green Park, Piccadilly
🚌 9, 14, 19, 22, 38

Name of Governing Body:
Alfred Dunhill Limited
Independent

All Hallows by the Tower Undercroft Museum

Byward Street
London EC3R 5BJ
☎ 071-481 2928

The collection (including a Roman pavement and Roman artefacts) illustrates the history of the church and the famous people connected with it.

Open by appointment
£ ++

W S
⊖ Tower Hill
DLR: Tower Gateway
⇌ Fenchurch St
🚌 15, 25, 42, 78, 100, X15, D1, D9, D11

Name of Governing Body:
All Hallows Church
Independent

Amalgamated Engineering and Electrical Union Collection

110 Peckham Road
London SE15 5EL
☎ 071-703 4231

History of the Union.

09.00-17.00 Mon-Fri by appointment
£ Free

S G
⊖ Oval
⇌ Peckham Rye
🚌 12, 36, 171, 702X

Name of Governing Body:
Amalgamated Engineering and Electrical Union
Independent

Apsley House, The Wellington Museum

149 Piccadilly
Hyde Park Corner
London W1V 9FA
☎ 071-499 5676

The Iron Duke's London Palace housing his famous collection of paintings, porcelain, silver, orders, decorations and personalia.

Closed for major refurbishment until mid 1994. Please call for details of opening hours and admission charges.
S G
⊖ Hyde Park Corner
⇌ Victoria
🚌 2A, 2B, 8, 9, 10, 14, 16, 19, 22, 36, 38, 52, 73, 74, 82, 137, 137A

Name of Governing Body:
Trustees of the Victoria and Albert Museum
National

Arts Council Collection

Arts Council of Great Britain
South Bank Centre
Royal Festival Hall
London SE1 8XX
☎ 071-921 0875

Largest collection of post-war contemporary art in the UK. The collection has no permanent exhibition space, many of the works being on permanent loan to other museums and galleries throughout Britain. Temporary exhibitions are held at the Royal Festival Hall and occasionally at the Hayward Gallery.

Limited access by appointment
£ Free (the Hayward charges)

✗
⊖ Embankment, Waterloo
⇌ Waterloo
🚌 1, 4, 26, 68, 76, 77, 149, 168, 171, 171A, 176, 188, 501, 505, 507, 511, 521, D1, P11

Name of Governing Body:
The Arts Council of Great Britain
National

Baden-Powell House

65 Queen's Gate
London SW7 5JS
☎ 071-584 7030

The Baden-Powell story, a permanent exhibition in words, sound and pictures on the life of the founder of the Boy Scout movement.

Bank of England Museum

09.00-18.00 Daily
£ Free
W G
⊖ South Kensington, Gloucester Rd
🚌 9, 9A, 10, 52, 74, C1

Name of Governing Body:
The Scout Association
Independent

Bank of England Museum

(entrance in Bartholomew Lane)
Threadneedle Street
London EC2R 8AH
☎ 071-601 5545

History of the Bank of England, including interactive videos illustrating contemporary banking.

10.00-17.00 Mon-Fri. 11.00-17.00 Sun and Public Hols (subject to review)
£ Free
A G
⊖ DLR: Bank, Monument
⇌ Liverpool St, Cannon St, Fenchurch St
🚌 8, 11, 15B, 21, 22B, 23, 25, 26, 76, 133, 149, 501, X15, D9

Name of Governing Body:
Governor and Company of the Bank of England
Independent

5

Barbican Art Gallery

Level 8
Barbican Centre
London EC2Y 8DS
☎ 071-638 4141 ext 7619

Programme of major temporary exhibitions. Occasional displays from the Corporation of London's permanent collection of works of art, which is curated at the Guildhall Art Gallery.

10.00-18.45 Mon, Wed, Thurs, Fri & Sat. 10.00-17.45 Tues, 12.00-18.45 Sun.
£ +++ Concessions
☕
✗
🅿
W E G
⊖ Moorgate, Barbican, St Paul's
⇌ Moorgate, Liverpool St
🚌 4, 8, 11, 21, 22B, 25, 43, 76, 141, 172, 214, 271, 521

Name of Governing Body:
Corporation of the City of London
Local Authority

Bankside Gallery

48 Hopton Street
London SE1 9JH
☎ 071-928 7521

Changing exhibitions of contemporary work by the Royal Watercolour Society and the Royal Society of Painter Printmakers. Historical exhibitions and educational programmes. Diploma collections of the two societies on loan to other museums.

During exhibitions only - 10.00-20.00 Tues, 10.00-17.00 Wed-Sat, 13.00-17.00 Sun. Closed Mons.
£ ++ Concessions
Ⅴ
X
⊖ Blackfriars, London Bridge, Waterloo
⇌ Blackfriars, London Bridge, Waterloo
🚌 45, 59, 63, 149, 172, P11

Name of Governing Body:
The Royal Watercolour Society and the Royal Society of Painter-Printmakers
Independent

Barnet Museum

31 Wood Street
Barnet
Herts EN5 4BE
☎ 081-440 8066
☎ 081-449 0321

Material relating to the local community.

14.30-16.30 Tues-Thurs, 10.00-12.00 & 14.30-16.30 Sat.
£ Free
W
⊖ High Barnet
⇌ New Barnet
🚌 84A, 107, 307, 326

Name of Governing Body:
Barnet and District Local History Society
Independent

Bayhurst Wood Country Park

Breakspear Road
North Harefield
Middlesex
☎ 0895-630078

Demonstrations of local woodland crafts based on a collection of historic forestry equipment and tools.

Open by appointment
£ Free
P
W
⊖ Ruislip
🚌 U1, U8

Name of Governing Body:
London Borough of Hillingdon
Local Authority

Ben Uri Art Society

4th Floor
21 Dean Street
London W1V 6NE
☎ 071-437 2852

Exhibitions of contemporary art as well as a permanent collection of over 500 works by Jewish artists including Bomberg, Gertler and Auerbach. A full programme of activities is provided for members of the Society, including lectures and concerts.

10.00-17.00 Mon-Thurs, 14.00-17.00 Sun

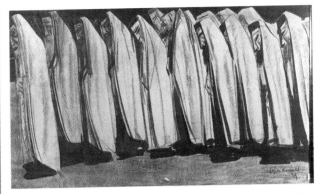

Ben Uri Art Society

£ Free
W
⊖ Tottenham Court Rd, Leicester Sq, Oxford Circus
≥ Charing Cross
🚌 7, 8, 10, 25, 55, 73, 98, 176

Name of Governing Body:
Ben Uri Art Society
Independent

Bethlem Royal Hospital Archives and Museum

The Bethlem Royal Hospital
Monks Orchard Road
Beckenham
Kent BR3 3BX
☎ 081-777 6611 ext 4307

Bethlem Royal Hospital Archives and Museum

7

Collections relating to history of psychiatry. Exhibition of works by artists suffering from mental disorder, including Richard Dadd, Louis Wain, Vaslav Nijinsky, Jonathan Martin, Charles Sims.

09.30-17.30 Mon-Fri. Please 'phone to confirm before visiting.
£ Free
P
X G
≹ Eden Park, East Croydon
🚍 119, 166, 194

Name of Governing Body:
The Bethlem Art and History Collections Trust
Independent

Bethnal Green Museum of Childhood

Cambridge Heath Road
London E2 9PA
☎ 081-980 4315/3204,
☎ 081-980 2415 Recorded info

The nation's collection of toys, dolls, dolls' houses, games and puppets, children's clothes and related furniture and accessories.

10.00-17.50 Mon-Thurs & Sat.
14.30-17.50 Sun
£ Free
P
W G
⊖ Bethnal Green
≹ Cambridge Heath
🚍 8, 26, 48, 55, 106, 253, D6

Name of Governing Body:
Trustees of the Victoria & Albert Museum
National

Bexley Museum

Hall Place
Bourne Road
Bexley
Kent DA5 1PQ
☎ 0322-526574 ext 221

Bexley local history collections including a Roman burial, natural history and Bexley's brickearths. Also temporary exhibition programme.

10.00-17.00 Mon-Sat, 14.00-18.00 Suns in summer. Closes dusk if earlier.
£ Free
S
≹ Bexley
🚍 89, 124, B15, 401, 492

Name of Governing Body:
London Borough of Bexley
Local Authority

Black Cultural Archives/Museum

378 Coldharbour Lane
Brixton
London SW9 8LF
☎ 071-738 4591

Temporary exhibitions based on the collection of African artefacts, slave papers, records and photographs and displays of work by black artists.

Museum 10.00-18.00 Mon-Sat, Archives 10.00-16.00 by appointment only.
£ Free
⊖ Brixton
≹ Brixton
🚍 2A, 2B, 3, 35, 37, 59, 109, 133, 159, 196, P4

Name of Governing Body:
The African Peoples Historical Monument Foundation (UK)
Independent

Boston Manor House

Boston Manor Road
Brentford
Middlesex
☎ 081-862 5808

Jacobean manor house with displays of local history.

14.00-16.30 Sun, 30 May-26 Sept.

Boston Manor House

£ Free
P
S
⊖ Boston Manor
⇌ Brentford
🚌 E8

Name of Governing Body:
**London Borough of
Hounslow**
Local Authority

Bramah Tea and Coffee Museum

Clove Building
Maguire Street
Butlers Wharf
London SE1 2NQ
☎ 071-378 0222

Teapots and coffee making
machines, both domestic and
commercial from 1650s to the
present day. Also advertising
material and packaging, cosies,
caddies, urns, cartoons and
paintings.

10.00-18.30 Daily. Closed
Christmas Day and Boxing Day.
£ ++ Concessions
V
☕
⊖ Tower Hill, London Bridge
DLR: Tower Gateway
⇌ London Bridge
🚌 15, 42, 47, 78, P11

Name of Governing Body:
Private collection
Independent

British Architectural Library Drawings Collection and RIBA Heinz Gallery

21 Portman Square
London W1H 9HF
☎ 071-580 5533

Bramah Tea and Coffee Museum

Major collection of drawings
and items relating to the history
and practice of architecture
c.1500 to the present day.
Temporary exhibitions are held
in the Heinz Gallery.

BAL Drawings Collection:
10.00-13.00 Mon-Fri, by
appointment only.
£ +++ Concessions

Heinz Gallery (during
exhibitions): 11.00-17.00 Mon-
Fri, 10.00-13.00 Sat.
£ Free
A G
⊖ Marble Arch, Baker St

9

🚌 2A, 2B, 13, 74, 82, 113, 139, 159, 274

Name of Governing Body:
Royal Institute of British Architects
Independent

British Council Collection

Visual Arts Department
11 Portland Place
London W1N 4EJ
☎ 071-389 3049

Major collection of C20th British art including paintings, sculpture, watercolours, graphics, photographs and mixed media works, mainly intended for world-wide circulating exhibitions.

Access by written appointment only
£ Free
🅿
⊖ Oxford Circus
🚌 3, 6, 7, 8, 10, 12, 13, 15, X15, 16A, 23, 25, 53, 55, 73, 88, 94, 98, 113, 135, 137, 139, 159, 176, C2

Name of Governing Body:
British Council
National

British Dental Association Museum

64 Wimpole Street
London W1M 8AL
☎ 071-935 0875 ext 209

Major collections relating to the history of dentistry.

09.00-17.00 Mon-Fri. Closed Bank Hols

£ Free
A
⊖ Regent's Park, Bond St
🚌 6, 7, 10, 13, 113

Name of Governing Body:
British Dental Association
Independent

British Museum

Great Russell Street
London WC1B 3DG
☎ 071-636 1555

National collection of antiquities, ethnography, prints, drawings, coins, medals and banknotes. The museum departments are: Greek and Roman, Egyptian, Japanese,

Prehistoric and Romano-British, Western Asiatic, Oriental, Coins and Medals, Medieval and Later, Prints and Drawings and Ethnography.

10.00-17.00 Mon-Sat; 14.30-18.00 Sun.
£ Free
☕
✗
W X G E
⊖ Tottenham Court Rd, Holborn, Russell Sq
🚌 7, 8, 10, 14, 14A, 19, 22B, 24, 25, 29, 30, 38, 55, 68, 73, 98, 134, 168, 176, 188

Name of Governing Body:
Trustees of the British Museum
National

British Optical Association Foundation Collection

c/o British College of
Optometrists
10 Knaresborough Place
London SW5 OTG
☎ 071-373 7765

History of spectacles and other
aids to vision from the Middle
Ages to the present. The
collection includes prints,
paintings and objets d'art, all
with an optical interest, as well
as optical instruments and
equipment.

10.00-16.00 Mon-Fri by
appointment only
⊖ Earl's Court
🚍 31, 74, C3

Name of Governing Body:
**British Optical Association
Foundation Trust**
Independent

British Oxygen Company Museum

(The Charles King Collection)
9 Bedford Square
London WC1B 3RA
☎ 071-631 1650

Historic anaesthetic apparatus.

Open for research by
appointment
£ Free
A G
⊖ Tottenham Court Rd,
Goodge St, Russell Sq
🚍 10, 14, 14A, 24, 29, 73, 134

Name of Governing Body:
**Association of Anaesthetists
of Great Britain & Ireland**
Independent

BT Museum

see Story of
Telecommunications

Bromley Museum

The Priory
Church Hill
Orpington BR6 OHH
☎ 0689-873826

Impressive medieval/post-
medieval building housing the
Avebury collection, local
archaeological material from the
Palaeolithic to the Early Saxon
periods, geological material and
expanding collections of social
history, dress and fine art.

09.00-17.00 Mon-Wed, Fri, Sat.
Closed Bank Hols.
£ Free
P
S G
🚉 Orpington
🚍 51, 61, 208, R1, R3, R4, R7,
R11

Name of Governing Body:
London Borough of Bromley
Local Authority

Brooking Collection

University of Greenwich
Dartford Campus
Oakfield Lane
Dartford
Kent DA1 2SZ
☎ 081-316 9897

Architectural detail ranging
from doors and windows to
timber mouldings and
bootscrapers from the grand to
the very ordinary. From the
C16th to date.

10.00-17.00 Mon-Fri by
appointment only
£ Free
P
🚉 Dartford
🚍 476, 478 and minibus from
Station to Campus during term
time.

Name of Governing Body:
**Brooking Architectural
Museum Trust**
Independent

Bruce Castle Museum

Lordship Lane
London N17 8NU
☎ 081-808 8772

Built in C16th, but substantially
altered in later years, Bruce
Castle was once the home of
Rowland Hill, the inventor of
the Penny Post, whose family
ran a boys' school in the
building. Displays include the
local history of Haringey, a fine
postal history collection and
temporary exhibitions.

13.00-17.00 Tues-Sun
£ Free
P
A G
⊖ Wood Green
🚉 Bruce Grove
🚍 123, 243, 243A

Name of Governing Body:
London Borough of Haringey
Local Authority

Brunel's Engine House

Tunnel Road
Rotherhithe
London SE16 4LF
☎ 081-318 2489
☎ 0708-447361

W G
⊖ Westminster
🚌 3, 11, 12, 24, 53, 77A, 88, 109, 159, 184, 196

Name of Governing Body:
Imperial War Museum
National

Carlyle's House

24 Cheyne Row
Chelsea
London SW3 5HL
☎ 071-352 7087

C18th town house, home of the writer Thomas Carlyle and his wife Jane from 1834 until their deaths. Contains books, personalia and furniture including an early piano played by Chopin.

Part of the temporary works for Marc Isambard Brunel's Thames Tunnel, the world's first underwater thoroughfare. The tunnel remains in use by London Underground, East London Line, and the Engine House is now a museum housing a restored steam engine and a display about the Thames Tunnel.

The underground emergency headquarters used by Winston Churchill and the British Government during WWII.

11.00-17.00 Wed-Sun & Bank Hol Mons Apr-Oct. Closed Good Friday.

10.00-18.00 Daily. Closed 24-26 Dec and 1 Jan.
£ +++ Concessions

12.00-16.00 First Sunday of each month or by appointment.
£+ Concessions
S
⊖ Rotherhithe
🚌 47,188,P11

Name of Governing Body:
Brunel Exhibition Rotherhithe
Independent

Cabinet War Rooms

Clive Steps
King Charles Street
London SW1A 2AQ
☎ 071-930 6961

Cabinet War Rooms

£ ++
S G
Ө South Kensington, Sloane Sq
🚌 11, 19, 22, 45A, 49, 219, 239, 249, 349

Name of Governing Body:
The National Trust
Independent

Carshalton Water Tower

Carshalton House
Pound Street
Carshalton
Surrey SM5 3PS
☎ 081-655 1640

Unique survival of C18th domestic architecture, the water tower is flanked by an orangery, bathroom and robing room.

Open days & groups by appointment - telephone for details
£ Telephone for details
🚃 Carshalton
🚌 127, 154, 157, 408, 413, 726

Name of Governing Body:
Carshalton Water Tower Trust
Independent

Centre for Medical Science and History

Wellcome Building
183 Euston Road
London NW1 2BE
☎ 071-611 8586 Enquiries

Opened in January 1993, the centre provides information and photographic services, a scientific meetings programme and interactive video discs as

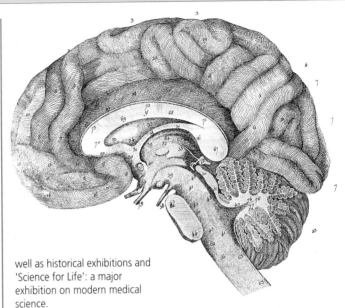

well as historical exhibitions and 'Science for Life': a major exhibition on modern medical science.

09.45-17.00 Mon-Fri
£ Free
Ө Euston, Euston Square
🚃 Euston
🚌 10, 14, 14A, 18, 73, 74, 253

Wellcome Institute for the History of Medicine

(Fourth Floor Exhibition)
183 Euston Road
London NW1 2BE
☎ 071-611 8546

Based primarily on the outstanding collections of the Wellcome Institute Library, the gallery presents a lively programme of exhibitions on the history of medicine. Three to four exhibitions are arranged each year.

09.45-17.00 Mon-Fri, 10.00-13.00 Sat.
£ Free
Travel details as above entry

Name of Governing Body:
The Wellcome Trust
Independent

Charles Darwin Memorial Museum

Down House
Luxted Road
Downe
Orpington
Kent BR6 7JT
☎ 0689-859119

Darwin memorabilia in the house in which he lived from 1842 until 1882.

13.00-18.00 Wed-Sun & Bank Hol Mons
£ + Concessions
🅿
X G
🚃 Bromley South
🚌 146

Name of Governing Body:
Royal College of Surgeons
Independent

Chartered Insurance Institute Museum

The Hall
20 Aldermanbury
London EC2V 7HY
☎ 071-606 3835

The largest collection of UK firemarks and fireplates. Collection of artefacts relating to the history of firefighting and fire insurance.

10.00-16.00 Mon-Fri
£ Free
S G
⊖ Moorgate, Bank, St Paul's
⇌ Moorgate
🚌 4, 8, 21, 22B, 25, 43, 76, 141, 172

Name of Governing Body:
Chartered Insurance Institute
Independent

Chelsea Physic Garden

66 Royal Hospital Road
London SW3 4HS
☎ 071-352 5646

A centre for display and research in botany and horticulture, founded by the Society of Apothecaries in 1673 to study medicinal herbs.

14.00-17.00 Sun & Wed, Apr-Oct. 12.00-17.00 during Chelsea Flower Show and Chelsea Festival week.
£ ++
👄 X G
⊖ Sloane Sq
🚌 11, 19, 22, 49, 137, 219, 239

Name of Governing Body:
Chelsea Physic Garden Co.
Independent

Chiswick House

Burlington Lane
Chiswick
London W4 2RP
☎ 081-995 0508

The ornate reception rooms of this C18th English Palladian villa are decorated in their original manner and adorned with some of the original pictures. The ground floor exhibition illustrates the evolution of the house and gardens.

10.00-16.00 Oct-Maundy Thurs
10.00-18.00 Good Friday-30 Sept. Closed Christmas Eve and Christmas Day.
£ ++ Concessions
🅿
S G
⊖ Turnham Green
⇌ Chiswick
🚌 E3, 190, 290

Name of Governing Body:
English Heritage
Nationally funded

Church Farm House Museum

Church Farm House Museum

Greyhound Hill
Hendon
London NW4 4JR
☎ 081-203 0130

Permanent displays of local history and domestic life. Programme of temporary exhibitions.

10.00-17.00 Mon-Thurs, 10.00-13.00 & 14.00-17.00 Sat, 14.00-17.30 Sun.
£ Free
P
S G
⊖ Hendon Central
⇌ West Hendon
🚌 113, 143, 143A, 183, 240, 326

Name of Governing Body:
London Borough of Barnet
Local Authority

Clockmakers' Company Collection

The Clock Room
Guildhall Library
Aldermanbury
London EC2P 2EJ
☎ 071-606 3030 ext 1865

Collection of timepieces mainly made by members of the Company since its formation in 1631, together with some specialist objects concerned with John Harrison and other great pioneers of chronometry. A major library and archive.

09.30-16.45 Mon-Fri
£ Free
X

⊖ St Paul's, Moorgate, Bank Mansion House
⇌ Liverpool St, Moorgate
🚌 4, 8, 11, 15B, 21, 22B, 25, 26, 43, 76, 133, 149, 172, 214, 501

Name of Governing Body:
Worshipful Company of Clockmakers
Independent

Commonwealth Institute

Kensington High Street
London W8 6NQ
☎ 071-603 4535

Discover the history, culture, wildlife, crafts and economies of the 50 Commonwealth countries through a programme of permanent and special exhibitions, cultural events and festivals and the Education Programme for schools. Contact Marketing and Publicity for a free copy of 'What's On'.

10.00-17.00 Mon-Sat, 14.00-17.00 Sun. Closed 24-26 Dec, 1 Jan, May Day and Good Friday.
£ Free
☕
W E G
⊖ High Street Kensington, Earl's Court, Holland Park
⇌ Kensington Olympia
🚌 9, 9A, 10, 27, 28, 31, 49, C1

Name of Governing Body:
Board of Governors of the Commonwealth Institute
National

£ Free
🍵
W G
⊖ Angel
⇌ King's Cross
🚌 4, 19, 30, 38, 43, 56, 73, 153, 171A, 214, X43

Name of Governing Body:
The Crafts Council
National

Croydon Natural History and Scientific Society

c/o 96a Brighton Road
South Croydon
Surrey CR2 6AD
☎ 081-688 2720

Collections relating to local geology, archaeology, natural and social history.

Open by appointment
£ Free
S
⇌ Woodmansterne
🚌 166

Name of Governing Body:
Croydon Natural History and Scientific Society Ltd
Independent

Courtauld Institute Galleries

Somerset House
Strand
London WC2R ORN
☎ 071-873 2526

Samuel Courtauld Collection of Impressionist and Post-Impressionist paintings, the Princes Gate Collection of Old Master paintings, the Lee and Gambier-Parry Collections and the Hunter Bequest.

10.00-18.00 Mon-Sat, 14.00-18.00 Sun
£ ++ Concessions
🍵
X G
⊖ Temple, Embankment, Covent Garden
⇌ Charing Cross

🚌 1, 4, 6, 9, 11, 13, 15, 23, 26, 68, 77A, 168, 171, 171A, 176, 188, 501, 505, 521

Name of Governing Body:
University of London
University

Crafts Council

44A Pentonville Road
London N1 9BY
☎ 071-278 7700

National centre for contemporary craft, housing the gallery as well as information centre, reference and picture libraries and loan collection.

10.00-17.00 Tues-Sat, 14.00-17.00 Sun.

Crystal Palace Museum

Anerley Hill
London SE19 2BA
☎ 081-676 0700

The story of Crystal Palace located in the last surviving building.

14.00-17.00 every Sunday
£ Free
🅿
⇌ Crystal Palace
🚌 2A, 3, 63, 122, 137A, 157, 202, 227, 249, 306

Name of Governing Body:
The Crystal Palace Museum Trust
Independent

Cuming Museum

155-157 Walworth Road
London SE17 1RS
☎ 071-701 1342

Southwark's history from Roman times to the present together with worldwide collections of the Cuming family and special exhibitions on local themes. A National Heritage 'Museum of the Year' Award winner in 1992.

10.00-17.00 Tues-Sat
£ Free
🅿
S G
♿ Elephant & Castle
🚆 Elephant & Castle
🚌 12, 35, 40, 45, 68, 171

Name of Governing Body:
London Borough of Southwark
Local Authority

Cutty Sark the Clipper Ship

King William Walk
Greenwich
London SE10 9HT
☎ 081-858 3445

Only surviving tea clipper, with displays chronicling the building and life of the ship. Also a large collection of merchant ship figureheads.

10.00-17.00 Mon-Sat, 12.00-17.00 Sun, Oct-Mar. 10.00-18.00 Mon-Sat, 12.00-18.00 Sun Apr-Sept.

£ ++ Concessions
S G
DLR: Island Gardens and foot tunnel
≋ Greenwich
🚌 177, 180, 188, 199, 286

Name of Governing Body:
Maritime Trust
Independent

Czech Memorial Scrolls Centre

Westminster Synagogue
Kent House
Rutland Gardens
Knightsbridge
London SW7 1BX
☎ 071-584 3741

Permanent exhibition tells the unique story of the rescue from Prague, in 1964, of 1,564 Torrah scrolls confiscated by the Nazis during WWII and their restoration and redistribution to communities throughout the world.

10.00-16.00 Tues & Thurs, other times by appointment
£ Free
⊖ Knightsbridge
🚌 9, 10, 14, 19, 22, 52, 74, 137, C1

Name of Governing Body:
Memorial Scrolls Trust
Independent

David Evans Craft Centre of Silk

Bourne Road
Crayford
Kent DA1 4BP
☎ 0322-559401

Story of silk from cocoon to finished product. Demonstrations of hand silk printing and a video room.

Guided tours available and special events planned for 1993, David Evans 150th Anniversary year. Please ring for programme.

09.30-17.00 Mon-Fri, 09.30-16.30 Sat.
£ + Concessions
🅿
X G
≋ Crayford
🚌 96, 492, 726

Name of Governing Body:
David Evans & Co
Independent

 17, 19, 38, 46, 55, 171A, 243, 505

Name of Governing Body:
Trustees of the Dickens House and Dickens House Fund
Independent

Diocesan Treasury in the Crypt of St Paul's Cathedral

Chapter House
St Paul's Churchyard
London EC4M 8AD
☎ 071-248 2705

Church plate and Cathedral treasures.

09.00-16.15 Mon-Sat
£ ++ Concessions
⊖ St Paul's
⇌ St Paul's Thameslink
🚌 4, 8, 11, 15, X15, 17, 22B, 23, 25, 26, 76, 172, 501, 521

Name of Governing Body:
Dean and Chapter of St Paul's
Independent

Down House

see Charles Darwin Memorial Museum

Dr Johnson's House

17 Gough Square
London EC4A 3DE
☎ 071-353 3745

Where Johnson compiled the first definitive English dictionary. Exhibits include portraits, letters and objects relating to Johnson and his circle.

Design Museum

Butlers Wharf
Shad Thames
London SE1 2YD
☎ 071-407 6261

Regularly changing exhibitions and displays which include cars, furniture, domestic appliances, cameras, graphics and ceramics offer an introduction to the role of design in our everyday lives from the origins of mass-production to the present day.

10.30-17.30 Daily.
£ ++ Concessions
📷
✗
🅿
W G
⊖ London Bridge, Tower Hill
DLR: Tower Gateway
⇌ London Bridge
🚌 15, 42, 47, 78, P11

Name of Governing Body:
The Conran Foundation
Independent

Dickens House Museum

48 Doughty Street
London WC1N 2LF
☎ 071-405 2127

Material relating to the life, works and times of Charles Dickens, collected together in one of his homes.

10.00-17.00 Mon-Sat. Closed Sun, Bank Hols and Christmas week.
£ ++ Concessions
S G
⊖ Russell Sq
⇌ King's Cross

11.00-17.00 Mon-Sat, Oct-Apr.
11.00-17.30 Mon-Sat, May-Sept. Closed Sun & Public Hols.
£ ++ Concessions
S G
⊖ Chancery Lane, Temple, Blackfriars
⇌ St Paul's Thameslink, Blackfriars

🚌 4, 11, 15, 23, 26, 45, 59, 63, 76, 172, 521

Name of Governing Body:
Trustees of Dr Johnson's House
Independent

Dulwich Picture Gallery

College Road
London SE21 7AD
☎ 081-693 5254
☎ 081-693 8000

England's oldest public art gallery housed in purpose-built gallery by Sir John Soane with important collections of C17th and C18th Old Master paintings, including works by Rembrandt, Rubens, Gainsborough and Poussin.

10.00-13.00, 14.00-17.00 Tues-Fri, 11.00-17.00 Sat, 14.00-17.00 Sun.

£ ++ Concessions
🅿
A G
⇌ West Dulwich, Nth Dulwich
🚌 3, 12, 37, 78, 176, 185, P4

Name of Governing Body:
Alleyn's College of God's Gift
Independent

East Ham Nature Reserve

Norman Road
East Ham
London E6 4HN
☎ 081-470 4525

Nine acre churchyard containing many species of birds, animals and plants. Recently won a Gulbenkian award for best provision for disabled visitors.

10.00-17.00 Mon-Fri, 14.00-17.00 Sat & Sun. Interpretation centre 14.00-17.00 Tues, Thurs, Sat, Sun. Hours under review please check before visiting.
£ Free
⊖ East Ham then bus
⇌ North Woolwich then bus
🚌 101, 104, D2

Name of Governing Body:
Governors of the Passmore Edwards Museum
Local Authority

Embroiderers' Guild

Apartment 41
Hampton Court Palace
East Molesey
Surrey KT8 9AU
☎ 081-943 1229

British and foreign embroidery from the C16th to the present day.

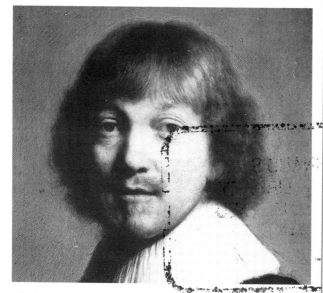

Dulwich Picture Gallery

0.30-16.00 Mon-Fri by
appointment only.
£ Free
P
River Launch from Richmond,
Westminster and Kingston
≋ Hampton Court
🚌 111, 131, 216, R68
Green Line 415, 716, 718, 726

Name of Governing Body:
The Embroiderers' Guild
Independent

Epping Forest Museum and Queen Elizabeth's Hunting Lodge

Rangers Road
Chingford
London E4 7QH
☎ 081-508 2266

Tudor royal hunting-grandstand
with displays illustrating the
history of Epping Forest.

Closed until late 1993
£ + Concessions
P
S G
⊖ Walthamstow Central
≋ Chingford
🚌 97, 97A, 179, 212, 313, 379, 444

Name of Governing Body:
Corporation of the City of London
Local Authority

Erith Museum

Erith Library
Walnut Tree Road
Erith
Kent DA8 1RS
☎ 0322-336582

Local history from prehistory to
recent times. Displays include
Lesnes Abbey, Hiram Maxim's
Flying Machine, local industries
and an Edwardian kitchen.

14.15-17.15 Mon & Wed,
14.15-17.00 Sat
£ Free
A G
≋ Erith
🚌 99, 229, 469, B12, B13

Name of Governing Body:
London Borough of Bexley
Local Authority

Fan Museum

12 Crooms Hill
Greenwich
London SE10 8ER
☎ 081-858 7879
☎ 081-305 1441

Fans and fan leaves with related
and explanatory material. Visits
to crafts/conservation
workshops by arrangement.
Changing thematic exhibitions
three times a year.

11.00-16.30 Tues-Sat, 12.00-16.30 Sun
£ ++ Concessions

🍴 Special bookings only
A
DLR: Island Gardens
≋ Greenwich
🚌 1, 177, 180, 185, 188, 286

Name of Governing Body:
The Fan Museum Trust Ltd
Independent

Fenton House

Hampstead Grove
London NW3 6RT
☎ 071-435 3471

Benton Fletcher collection of
early keyboard instruments and
the Binnings collection of
English and continental
porcelain.

14.00-18.00 Sat & Sun in Mar.
13.00-19.00 Mon, Tues & Wed,
11.00-18.00 Sat, Sun & Bank
Hols Apr-end Oct. Last
admission half hour before
closing.
£ ++
S G
⊖ Hampstead
🚌 46, C11, 268

Name of Governing Body:
The National Trust
Independent

Florence Nightingale Museum

2 Lambeth Palace Road
London SE1 7EW
☎ 071-620 0374

Collection of personal memorabilia and other items relating to the life and times of Florence Nightingale, housed on the site of St Thomas's Hospital.

10.00-16.00 Tues-Sun and Bank Hol Mons.
£ + + Concessions
🅿
W G
⊖ Waterloo, Westminster
⇌ Waterloo
🚌 12, 53, 77, 109, 171, 171A, 184, 196, 507, D1, P11

Name of Governing Body:
The Florence Nightingale Museum Trust
Independent

Forty Hall Museum

Forty Hill
Enfield
Middlesex EN2 9HA
☎ 081-363 8196
☎ 081-367 9098

Built in 1629, the house retains much of its original interior. Displays of local history and fine and applied art.

10.00-17.00 Tues-Sun
£ Free
☕
🅿
X G
⇌ Enfield Chase, Enfield Town, Gordon Hill
🚌 191, 231

Name of Governing Body:
London Borough of Enfield
Local Authority

Frederick W. Paine Museum

Bryson House
Horace Road
Kingston-upon-Thames
Surrey KT1 2SL
☎ 081-546 7472

The history of the Frederick W. Paine company of undertakers and the activities of associated companies.

Open by appointment
£ Free
🅿

🚌 71, 281, 406, 479, 578, K1, K2, K3, K4,

Name of Governing Body:
The Great Southern Group plc
Independent

Freud Museum

20 Maresfield Gardens
London NW3 5SX
☎ 071-435 2002/5167

Freud's London home containing his consulting rooms with library, antiquity collection and furniture from Vienna: exhibitions and archive films on view.

12.00-17.00 Weds-Sun (other times by appointment).
£ ++
S G
⊖ Finchley Rd
⇌ Finchley Rd & Frognal
🚌 13, 46, 82, 113, 268, C11, C12

Name of Governing Body:
Sigmund Freud Archives Inc
Independent

Freud Museum

Geffrye Museum

Kingsland Road
London E2 8EA
☎ 071-739 9893

Early C18th almshouses containing period room reconstructions and fine furniture collection 1600-1950s. Walled herb garden open Apr-Oct.

10.00-17.00 Tues-Sat, 14.00-17.00 Sun & Bank Hol Mons.
£ Free
◗
W G
⊖ Old St, Liverpool St then bus
⇌ Old St, Liverpool St
🚍 22A, 22B, 67, 149, 243, 243A

Name of Governing Body:
Geffrye Museum Trust
Independent

Gillette UK Ltd

Great West Road
Isleworth
Middlesex TW7 5NP
☎ 081-560 1234

Collection of items relating to the history of shaving.

Open for research by appointment
£ Free
⊖ Osterley
🚍 H91

Name of Governing Body:
Gillette UK Ltd
Independent

Gordon Museum

UMDS
(Guy's Campus)
London SE1 9RT
☎ 071-955 4358

Major collection of pathological, anatomical and dermatological material used in the teaching of medicine and a small collection of historical artefacts associated with the history of Guy's Hospital.

09.00-17.00 Mon-Fri by appointment to those people associated with the medical profession.

£ Free
⊖ London Bridge
⇌ London Bridge
🚍 17, 21, 22A, 35, 40, 43, 47, 48, 133, 214, 344, 501, 505, 521, D1, D11, P3, P11

Name of Governing Body:
United Medical and Dental Schools
Independent

Government Art Collection

St Christopher House Annexe
Sumner Street
London SE1 9LA
☎ 071-928 9403

One of the largest holdings of British art of all periods. The works are on display in British government buildings at home and abroad.

Open for research by appointment
£ Free
🅿
X
⊖ Blackfriars, London Bridge, Waterloo
⇌ Blackfriars, London Bridge, Waterloo
🚍 45, 59, 63, 172, 344, P11

Name of Governing Body:
HM Government
National

Grange Museum of Community History

On Neasden Roundabout
Neasden Lane
London NW10
☎ 081-452 8311

Converted C18th stableblock containing period room settings

23

and multicultural displays of local history.

11.00-17.00 Tues, Thurs, Fri. 11.00-20.00 Wed, 10.00-12.00 & 13.00-17.00 Sat. 11.00-17.00 Mons Sept-May. 14.00-17.00 Suns in Jun-Aug.
£ Free
Ⓥ
Ⓟ
S G
⊖ Neasden
🚍 16, 92, 112, 182, 245, 297

Name of Governing Body:
London Borough of Brent
Local Authority

Greenwich Borough Museum

232 Plumstead High Street
London SE18 1JL
☎ 081-855 3240

Archaeology, social history and natural history relating to Greenwich, Woolwich, Eltham, Deptford, Charlton, Plumstead and the new town of Thamesmead. Also a programme of temporary exhibitions, schools service, holiday activities and Saturday Club.

14.00-19.00 Mon, 10.00-13.00 & 14.00-17.00 Tues, Thurs, Fri and Sat. Closed Sun and Wed.
£ Free
S
➤ Plumstead
🚍 96, 99, 122, 180

Name of Governing Body:
London Borough of Greenwich
Local Authority

Guards Museum

Wellington Barracks
Birdcage Walk
London SW1E 6HQ
☎ 071-414 3271

A splendid collection of uniforms, weapons and memorabilia illustrating the story of The Queen's Regiments of Foot Guards through their martial history and service to the Sovereign and the City of London for over three centuries.

10.00-16.00 Sat-Thurs
£ ++ Concessions
X G
⊖ St James's Park
➤ Victoria
🚍 2A, 2B, 11, 16, 24, 29, 36, 36B, 38, 52, 52A, 73, 82, 135, C1

Name of Governing Body:
HQ Household Division
Independent

Guildhall Art Gallery

Aldermanbury
London EC2P 2EJ
☎ 071-260 1632

The Corporation of London's permanent collection of London topography, Pre-Raphaelite and C19th works, and paintings by Sir Matthew Smith. New permanent gallery planned for 1996.

Open by appointment.
£ Free
A
⊖ St Paul's, Moorgate, Bank, Mansion House
➤ Moorgate, Liverpool St
🚍 4, 8, 11, 15B, 21, 22B, 25, 26, 43, 76, 133, 149, 172, 214, 501

Name of Governing Body:
Corporation of the City of London
Local Authority

Guildhall Library

(Print Room)
Aldermanbury
London EC2P 2EJ
☎ 071-260 1839

Prints, photographs, drawings, maps, plans, theatre programmes, theatre bills, portraits and other ephemera relating to London. Also a collection of Old Master Prints.

09.30-17.00 Mon-Fri
£ Free
X
⊖ St Paul's, Moorgate, Bank, Mansion House
➤ Moorgate, Liverpool St
🚍 4, 8, 11, 15B, 21, 22B, 25, 26, 43, 76, 133, 149, 172, 214, 501

Name of Governing Body:
Corporation of the City of London
Local Authority

Guinness Archives

Hop Store No 2
Park Royal Brewery
Park Royal
London NW10 7RR
☎ 081-965 7700 ext 3975

Statutory and business records, plus advertising material and artefacts relating to Guinness.

Open for research by appointment
£ Free
P
⊖ Park Royal, Hanger Lane
🚌 83, 105, 112, 187

Name of Governing Body:
Guinness Brewing Worldwide Ltd
Independent

Gunnersbury Park Museum

Gunnersbury Park
London W3 8LQ
☎ 081-992 1612

Local history museum for Ealing and Hounslow set in a splendid mansion, home of the Rothschild family until 1925. Displays include costume, carriages and temporary exhibitions. Original Victorian kitchens open summer weekends.

13.00-17.00 Mon-Fri, 13.00-18.00 Sat, Sun & Bank Hols Apr-Oct. 13.00-16.00 Daily Nov-Mar. Closed some Public Hols.
£ Free
☕
P
A G
⊖ Acton Town

≋ Gunnersbury
🚌 E3 Daily, 7 Sundays

Name of Governing Body:
London Borough of Hounslow (on behalf of the London Boroughs of Ealing and Hounslow)
Local Authority

Hackney Museum

Central Hall
Mare Street
London E8 1HE
☎ 081-986 6914

Social history and visual arts, concentrating on the history of Hackney and the world-wide roots of Hackney people.

10.30-12.30 & 13.30-17.00 Tues-Fri, 13.30-17.00 Sat
£ Free
W G
≋ Hackney Central
🚌 22A, 22B, 30, 38, 48, 55, 106, 236, 253, 276, 277, D6, W15

Name of Governing Body:
London Borough of Hackney
Local Authority

Ham House

Ham Street
Richmond
Surrey TW10 7RS
☎ 081-940 1950

Furnished C17th mansion house.

Closed for refurbishment until Spring 1994. Call for details of opening hours and admission charges.
☕
X G
⊖ Richmond
≋ Richmond
🚌 371

Name of Governing Body:
National Trust
Independent

Hampstead Museum

Burgh House
New End Square
London NW3 1LT
☎ 071-431 0144

The local history of Hampstead, including its C18th Spa, writers and artists, especially Constable and Helen Allingham.

Hackney Museum

25

12.00-17.00 Weds-Sun, 14.00-17.00 Bank Hols. Closed Good Friday and Christmas period.
£ Free

✖
S A
⊖ Hampstead
⇌ Hampstead Heath
🚌 268, 24, 46, C11

Name of Governing Body:
Burgh House Trust
Independent

Hampton Court Palace

East Molesey
Surrey KT8 9AU
☎ 081-977 8441

Riverside Palace of Henry VIII with later additions by Sir Christopher Wren. Formal gardens, state apartments, Tudor kitchens, Mantegna cartoons, maze, great vine and Royal Tennis Court.

09.30-18.00 mid Mar-mid Oct daily, 09.30-16.30 mid Oct-mid Mar. Royal Tennis Court and Banqueting House closed during winter months.
£ +++ Concessions

✖
🅿
A G
River Launch from Richmond, Westminster & Kingston
⇌ Hampton Court
🚌 111, 131, 216, R68
Green Line 415, 716, 718, 726

Name of Governing Body:
Historic Royal Palaces Agency
National

Harrow Museum and Heritage Centre

Headstone Manor
Pinner View
Harrow
Middlesex HA2 6PX
☎ 081-861 2626

Local history collection, concentrating on domestic

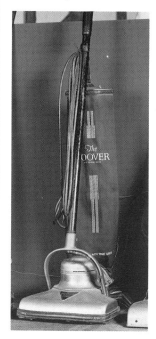

artefacts and Whitefriars Glassworks collection. Medieval moated Manor House and C16th Tithe Barn.

12.30-17.00 Wed-Fri, 10.30-17.00 Sat, Sun & Public Hols. Closes at dusk in winter.
£ Free

🅿
W G
⊖ Harrow on the Hill
⇌ Harrow & Wealdstone
🚌 H10, H14, H15, 350

Name of Governing Body:
Harrow Arts Council
Independent

Harrow School Old Speech Room Gallery

Church Hill
Harrow on the Hill
Middlesex HA1 3HP
☎ 081-869 1205
☎ 081-422 2196

Varied collection of Egyptian, Greek and Roman antiquities, English watercolours, modern British paintings, printed books, Harroviana and natural history.

14.30-17.00 Daily except Wed in term time, 14.30-17.00 Mon-Fri in holidays. Please confirm before visiting.
£ Free
S
⊖ Harrow on the Hill, South Harrow
⇌ Harrow on the Hill
🚌 258, H17

Name of Governing Body:
The Keepers and Governors of Harrow School
Independent

Heritage Centre, Honeywood

Honeywood Walk
Carshalton
Surrey SM5 3NX
☎ 081-773 4555

Permanent displays on the history of the area now covered by the London Borough of Sutton, plus changing programme of exhibitions; set in a C17th listed building, with later additions. Features magnificent Edwardian billiard room.

10.00-17.30 Tues-Sun.
£ + free on Thurs
☕
🅿
⇌ Carshalton
🚌 127, 154, 157, 408, 413, 726,

Name of Governing Body:
London Borough of Sutton
Local Authority

HM Tower of London

Tower Hill
London EC3N 4AB
☎ 071-709 0765

The Tower, begun in the C11th, has been fortress, palace and prison. Today it houses the Royal Armouries and the Crown Jewels.

09.30-17.00 Mon-Sat, Nov-Feb.
09.30-18.00 Mon-Sat & 10.00-18.00 Sun, Mar-Oct. Last tickets sold one hour before closing.
£ +++ Concessions
☕ on wharf
S G
⊖ Tower Hill

⇌ Fenchurch St, London Bridge
🚌 15, 42, 78, 100, D1, D9, D11

Name of Governing Body:
Department of National Heritage
National

HMS Belfast

Morgan's Lane
(off Tooley Street)
London SE1 2JH
☎ 071-407 6434

Launched in 1939, HMS Belfast is Europe's largest preserved WWII warship, now permanently moored close to London Bridge. Visitors can discover how sailors lived and fought on board as they explore all seven decks of this magnificent cruiser.

10.00-17.30 Daily Mar-Oct.
10.00-16.00 Daily Nov-Mar.
£ +++ Concessions
✕
S
⊖ Monument, London Bridge, Tower Hill
Ferry from Tower Hill pier
⇌ London Bridge
🚌 17, 21, 22A, 35, 40, 43, 47, 48, 133, 344, 501, 505, 521, D1, D11, P3, P11

Name of Governing Body:
Imperial War Museum
National

Hogarth's House

Hogarth Lane
Great West Road
London W4 2QN
☎ 081-994 6757

The artist's country house containing a permanent exhibition of engravings and reproduction paintings.

11.00-18.00 Mon-Sat (closed Tues) 14.00-18.00 Sun, Apr-Sept. 11.00-16.00 Mon-Sat (closed Tues) 14.00-16.00 Sun, Oct-Mar. Closed first two weeks of Sept each year.
£ Free
S G
⊖ Turnham Green
🚌 27, 290, E3, 267

Name of Governing Body:
London Borough of Hounslow
Local Authority

Horniman Museum and Gardens

100 London Road
Forest Hill
London SE23 3PQ
☎ 081-699 2339/1872/4911

Important collections of ethnography, musical instruments and natural history illustrating the world we live in - our cultures, arts, crafts, music and natural environment. Displays include a new aquarium. The museum is set in 16 acres of beautiful gardens and park.

10.30-17.30 Mon-Sat, 14.00-17.30 Sun
£ Free
☕
E X
🚃 Forest Hill
🚌 63, 78, 115, 122, 171, 176, 185, 194, 312, P4

Name of Governing Body:
Horniman Public Museum & Public Park Trust
Independent

Hospital for Sick Children

Peter Pan Gallery
55 Great Ormond Street
London WC1N 3JH
☎ 071-405 9200
ext 5920/5701

Archives, photographs and a small collection of decorative and scientific objects.

Open by appointment
£ Free
⊖ Russell Sq, Holborn
🚃 King's Cross, Euston
🚌 7, 8, 19, 22B, 25, 38, 55, 68, 168, 188, 196, 501, 505, X68

Name of Governing Body:
The Hospitals for Sick Children Special Health Authority
Independent

Hunterian Museum

The Royal College of Surgeons of England
35-43 Lincoln's Inn Fields
London WC2A 3PN
☎ 071-405 3474 ext 3011

Based on the collection of comparative and morbid anatomy founded by John Hunter FRS (1728-1793). Also definitive collection of pre-Listerian surgical instruments.

10.00-17.00 Mon-Fri by appointment for members of medical professions, students and researchers.
£ Free
A
⊖ Holborn, Temple
🚌 1, 8, 22B, 25, 68, 168, 171, 188, 501, 505, 521

Name of Governing Body:
The Royal College of Surgeons of England and the Board of Trustees of the Hunterian Collection
Independent

Imperial War Museum

Lambeth Road
London SE1 6HZ
☎ 071-416 5000
☎ 071 820 1683 Recorded info

National collection documenting the two world wars, and other aspects of C20th history involving Britain and the Commonwealth since 1914. Includes the Blitz experience, Trench experience and Operation Jericho.

10.00-18.00 Daily. Closed Christmas Eve, Christmas Day, Boxing Day and New Years Day.

£ ++ Concessions
✗
✗ G
⊖ Lambeth North, Elephant & Castle
⇌ Waterloo
🚌 1, 3, 12, 53, 59, 63, 68, 109, 159, 171, 188, 344, C10

Name of Governing Body:
Trustees of the Imperial War Museum
National

Inns of Court and City Yeomanry Museum

10 Stone Buildings
Lincoln's Inn Fields
London WC2A 3TG
☎ 071-405 8112

Small collection of uniforms, equipment, medals, prints etc of the Inns of Court Regiments and the City of London Yeomanry (the Rough Riders) during the period of 1798 to the present day.

Tuesdays, by appointment only
£ Free
⊖ Holborn, Temple, Chancery Lane
🚌 1, 8, 22B, 25, 68, 98, 171, 188, 501, 505, 521

Name of Governing Body:
Inns of Court and City Yeomanry Museum Trust
Independent

Institute of Ophthalmology Visual Sciences Collection

Bath Street
London EC1V 9EL
☎ 071-608 6800

Collection of instruments used for eye surgery. Following relocation the collection is not currently available for viewing. Planned to reopen Autumn 1993.

£ Free
⊖ Old Street
⇌ Old Street
🚌 5, 43, 55, 76, 141, 214, 243, 271, 505, D3

Name of Governing Body:
Institute of Ophthalmology
Independent

Island History Trust

Island House
Roserton Street
London E14 3PG
☎ 071-987 6041

Large collection of photographs illustrating family and community life on the Isle of Dogs from the 1880s to 1980s.

29

13.30-16.30 Tues, Wed & Fri.
£ Free
S G X
DLR: Crossharbour
🚌 277, D7, D8, D9, P14

Name of Governing Body:
Island History Trust
Independent

Iveagh Bequest, Kenwood

Hampstead Lane
London NW3 7JR
☎ 081-348 1286

Adam mansion on the borders of Hampstead Heath. Contains the Iveagh Bequest of Old Master and British paintings, including works by Rembrandt, Vermeer, Frans Hals, Turner, Gainsborough and Reynolds; a fine collection of neo-classical furniture; collections of C18th jewellery and silver shoe buckles.

10.00-16.00 Oct-Maundy Thursday, 10.00-18.00 Good Fri-30 Sept. Closed Christmas Eve and Christmas Day.
£ Free
✕
🅿
W G
⊖ Archway or Golders Green then 210 bus
🚌 210

Name of Governing Body:
English Heritage
Nationally funded

Jewish Museum

Woburn House
Tavistock Square
London WC1H OEP
☎ 071-388 4525

A collection of ceremonial art, antiquities and portraits illustrating Jewish life, history and religion, particularly in

Britain. Audiovisual programmes explain Jewish festivals and ceremonies.

10.00-16.00 Tues-Fri & Sun Apr-Sept. 10.00-13.00 Sun & Fri Oct-Mar. Closed Mon, Sat, Public Hols and Jewish Festivals.
£ Free
X G
⊖ Euston, Russell Sq, Euston Sq
🚆 Euston
🚌 14, 18, 30, 68, 73, 77A, 188

Name of Governing Body:
The Jewish Museum
Independent

Keats House

Keats Grove
Hampstead
London NW3 2RR
☎ 071-435 2062

Furnished Regency home of the poet John Keats, containing letters, books and relics of Keats, his circle and family. Keats Memorial Library (8,000 volumes) and the Kate Greenaway Collection by appointment only.

10.00-13.00, 14.00-18.00 Mon-Fri, 10.00-13.00, 14.00-17.00 Sat, 14.00-17.00 Sun & Bank Hols Apr-Oct. 13.00-17.00 Mon-Fri Nov-Mar, Sat & Sun as summer. Please confirm as winter hours subject to change.
£ ++
S G
⊖ Hampstead, Belsize Park
⇌ Hampstead Heath
🚌 24, 46, 168, 268, C11

Name of Governing Body:
London Borough of Camden
Local Authority

Kensington Palace, State Apartments & Royal Ceremonial Dress Collection

Kensington Palace
London W8 4PX
☎ 071-937 9561

State apartments occupied by William & Mary, George I and II, rooms lived in by Queen Victoria. Displays of ceremonial dress and uniform.

Open throughout the year, please call to confirm hours.
£ +++ Concessions
☕
S G
⊖ Notting Hill Gate, Queensway, High Street Kensington
🚌 9, 9A, 10, 12, 27, 28, 49, 52, 70, 94, C1

Name of Governing Body:
Historic Royal Palaces Agency
National

Kenwood House

see Iveagh Bequest, Kenwood

Kew Bridge Steam Museum

Green Dragon Lane
Brentford
Middlesex TW8 0EN
☎ 081-568 4757

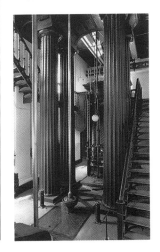

Unique collection of large steam pumping engines, housed in a former Victorian waterworks. Includes the world's largest working beam engine. Schools service.

11.00-17.00 Daily. In steam at weekends only.
£ ++ Concessions
☕ Weekends only
P
X G
⊖ Gunnersbury
⇌ Kew Bridge
🚌 7, 65, 237, 267, 391

Name of Governing Body:
Kew Bridge Engines Trust & Water Supply Museum Ltd
Independent

Kew Collections of Economic Botany

Royal Botanic Gardens
Kew
Richmond
Surrey TW9 3AB
☎ 081-940 1171

70,000 items, including foods, beverages, fibres, fabrics, paper dyes, medicinal compounds, gums, resins, rubber and timber which have been put to economic use by people from all parts of the world.

Open to researchers by appointment.
£ Subject to review, Concessions
☕
X
P
⊖ Kew Gardens
⇌ Kew Gardens, Kew Bridge
🚌 65, 391

✗
W G
⊖ Kew Gardens
⇌ Kew Gardens, Kew Bridge
🚌 65, 391

Name of Governing Body:
Historic Royal Palaces Agency
National

Kingston-upon-Thames Museum and Heritage Centre

Wheatfield Way
Kingston-upon-Thames
Surrey KT1 2PS
☎ 081-547 6755 Enquiries

Kingston Museum and Heritage Centre is temporarily closed until mid 1993. It will reopen with new displays telling the story of Kingston-upon-Thames and an art gallery on the first floor.

£ Free
⇌ Kingston
🚌 65

Name of Governing Body:
Royal Borough of Kingston-upon-Thames
Local Authority

Name of Governing Body:
Trustees of the Royal Botanic Gardens, Kew
National

Kew Gardens Gallery

Royal Botanic Gardens
Kew
Richmond
Surrey TW9 3AB
☎ 081-940 1171

Exhibitions of the best of contemporary and historical flower paintings and botanical illustration. Includes paintings for sale.

Telephone for current opening times
£ Subject to review, Concessions

✗
🅿
⊖ Kew Gardens

⇌ Kew Gardens, Kew Bridge
🚌 65, 391

Name of Governing Body:
Trustees of the Royal Botanic Gardens, Kew
National

Kew Palace & Queen Charlotte's Cottage

Royal Botanic Gardens
Kew
Richmond
Surrey TW9 3AB
☎ 081-940 1171

Built in 1631, the Palace today reflects the private lives of George III and Queen Charlotte who used it as their family retreat.

Telephone for current opening times
£ + Concessions

Kirkaldy Testing Museum (Southwark)

99 Southwark Street
London SE1 OJF
☎ 0322-332195

Housed in the purpose-built building of 1874 is the original all-purpose materials testing machine designed by David Kirkaldy (1820-97). With this machine and others the museum aims to demonstrate the standardisation of materials testing developed by David Kirkaldy and the long history of the family works.

Open by appointment only
£ ++ Concessions
⊖ London Bridge
⇌ London Bridge
🚌 17, 21, 22A, 35, 40, 43, X43, 47, 48, 133, 214, 344, 501, 505, 521, D1, P11

Name of Governing Body:
The Kirkaldy Museum Trust Ltd
Independent

Knightscote Farm

Breakspear Road
Harefield
Middlesex
☎ 0895-50111 ext 2352

A collection of old farm machinery and tools dating to the 1940s.

Open by appointment only

£ Free
🅿
⊖ Ruislip
🚌 U1, U8

Name of Governing Body:
London Borough of Hillingdon
Local Authority

Leighton House Museum

12 Holland Park Road
London W14 8LZ
☎ 071-602 3316

Purpose-built studio house belonging to the Victorian painter, Lord Leighton, with spectacular Arab Hall incorporating Isnik tiles of the C16th and C17th. Collection includes furniture, ceramics and paintings by Leighton and his contemporaries.

11.00-17.50 Mon-Sat. Closed Sun and Public Hols.
£ Free
W G
⊖ High Street Kensington
🚌 9, 9A, 10, 27, 28, 31, 49

Name of Governing Body:
Royal Borough of Kensington and Chelsea
Local Authority

Library and Museum of the United Grand Lodge of England

Freemasons' Hall
Great Queen Street
London WC2B 5AZ
☎ 071-831 9811

Masonic regalia, medals, portraits and decorative arts items that have been used for Masonic purposes or have Masonic decoration. Worldwide collections concentrating on English Freemasonry.

10.00-17.00 Mon-Fri, 10.00-13.00 Sat. Closed Public Hols and preceding Sats.
£ Free
⊖ Covent Garden, Holborn
🚌 1, 8, 19, 22B, 25, 30, 38, 55, 68, X68, 98, 168, 171, 188, 196, 501, 505, 521

Name of Governing Body:
United Grand Lodge of Free and Accepted Masons of England
Independent

Linley Sambourne House

18 Stafford Terrace
London W8 7BH
☎ 071-994 1019

Unique survival of a late Victorian town house with original decorations, fixtures and furniture. The home of Punch illustrator Linley Sambourne (1844-1910), it is an

Leighton House Museum

example of a successful artist's house in 'artistic' Kensington.

10.00-16.00 Weds. 14.00-17.00 Sun, Mar-Oct
£ ++ Concessions
S
⊖ High St Kensington
🚍 9, 9A, 10, 27, 28, 31, 49, 52, 70, C1

Name of Governing Body:
Royal Borough of Kensington and Chelsea
(managed by The Victorian Society)
Local Authority

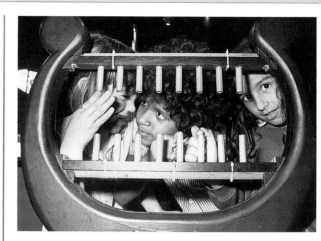

Little Holland House

40 Beeches Avenue
Carshalton
Surrey SM5 3LW
☎ 081-647 5168
☎ 081-773 4555

Home of Frank Dickinson (1874-1961) artist, designer and craftsman, inspired by William Morris and John Ruskin. The Grade II listed interior features paintings, hand made furniture and craft objects.

13.00-18.00 first Sunday of each month and Bank Hols from Mar-Oct inclusive.
£ +
🚆 Carshalton Beeches
🚍 154, 408, 726

Name of Governing Body:
London Borough of Sutton
Local Authority

Livesey Museum

682 Old Kent Road
London SE15 1JF
☎ 071-639 5604

Changing programme of temporary 'hands-on' exhibitions, aimed at families and children.

10.00-17.00 Mon-Sat
£ Free
A G
⊖ Elephant & Castle then bus
🚆 Elephant & Castle or Queen's Rd then bus
🚍 21, 53, 78, 172, 177, P11, P13

Name of Governing Body:
London Borough of Southwark
Local Authority

London Canal Museum

12/13 New Wharf Road
King's Cross
London N1 9RT
☎ 071-713 0836

Located in a former Victorian ice house, there are displays on the people, vessels, trade and wildlife of the Capital's canals. Also displays on the ice trade and an industrial ice well on show.

10.00-16.30 Tues-Sun. Last admission 15.45. Open Bank Hols except 24-26 Dec, 1-2 Jan.
£ ++ Concessions
⊖ King's Cross
🚆 King's Cross
🚍 10, 14A, 17, 18, 30, 45, 46, 63, 73, 74, 214, 259, C12

Name of Governing Body:
Canal Museum Trust
Independent

London Chest Hospital

Bonner Road
London E2 9JX
☎ 081-980 4433

Small collection of historic instruments relating to chest medicine and hospital archives.

Open by written appointment
£ Free
⊖ Bethnal Green
⇌ Cambridge Heath
🚌 8, 55, 106, 253, D6

Name of Governing Body:
National Heart & Chest Hospitals
Independent

London Fire Brigade Museum

Winchester House
94a Southwark Bridge Road
London SE1 0EG
☎ 071-587 4273

History of the Fire Brigade

Guided tours by appointment only
£ Free, subject to review
S
⊖ Borough
⇌ London Bridge
🚌 344

Name of Governing Body:
LFCDA
Independent

London Gas Museum

North Thames Gas
Twelvetrees Crescent
Bromley-by-Bow
London E3 3JH
☎ 071-987 2000 ext 3344

History of the gas industry.

09.00-16.00 Mon-Fri, by appointment. Open evenings and weekends by appointment to groups (charge).
£ Free
✗
🅿
⊖ Bromley-by-Bow
🚌 108, 278, S2, D4

Name of Governing Body:
British Gas plc
Independent

London Irish Rifles

Duke of York's HQ
King's Road
Chelsea
London SW3 4RX
☎ 071-930 4466 ext 5406

Items and documents of the London Irish Rifles (TA) from 1859, the year of formation.

Open by appointment
£ Free
⊖ Sloane Sq
⇌ Victoria
🚌 11, 19, 22, 137, 137A, 219, C1

Name of Governing Body:
London Irish Rifles Regimental Association
Independent

London Museum of Jewish Life

The Sternberg Centre
80 East End Road
Finchley
London N3 2SY
☎ 081-346 2288
☎ 081-349 1143

A museum of Jewish social history which preserves and records the history of Jewish London and the diverse roots and culture of Jewish people now living in Britain. Collections include documents, photographs and oral history archives. Educational programmes, guided walks and travelling exhibitions for loan to museums and other organisations.

10.30-17.00 Mon-Thurs, 10.30-16.30 Sun (except Aug & Bank Hol weekends). Closed Jewish Festivals, Public Hols and 24 Dec-4 Jan.
£ +
✗
S G
⊖ Finchley Central
🚌 13, 82, 112, 143, 260

Name of Governing Body:
Trustees of the London Museum of Jewish Life
Independent

35

London Scottish Regimental Museum

95 Horseferry Road
London SW1
☎ 071-630 1639

Regimental history.

Wed evenings, by appointment only
£ Free
⊖ St James's Park
⇌ Victoria
🚌 11, 24, 88, 507, 511, C10

Name of Governing Body:
The London Scottish Regimental Trust
Independent

London Toy and Model Museum

21/23 Craven Hill
London W2 3EN
☎ 071-262 9450
☎ 071-262 7905 Recorded information

Comprehensive collection of commercially made toys and models. Large garden with working railways.

London Toy and Model Museum

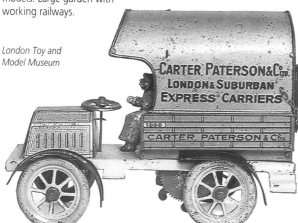

10.00-17.30 Tues-Sat. 11.00-17.30 Sun & Bank Hols
£ ++ Concessions
🍴
S
⊖ Queensway
⇌ Paddington
🚌 12, 70, 94

Name of Governing Body:
The Toy Museum Ltd
Independent

London Transport Museum

Covent Garden
London WC2E 7BB
☎ 071-379 6344
☎ 071-836 8557 Recorded information

The story of the world's largest urban passenger transport system and its impact on the growth of London and its suburbs illustrated by interactive exhibits, video displays, posters, models and photographs.

The museum will be closed 8 Mar-Dec 1993. It will re-open with major new displays; please

call to confirm opening hours and admission charges.
£
W G
⊖ Covent Garden
⇌ Charing Cross
🚌 1, 6, 9, 11, 13, 15, X15, 23, 26, 68, X68, 76, 77A, 168, 171, 171A, 176, 188, 505

Name of Governing Body:
London Regional Transport
Independent

Marble Hill House

Richmond Road
Twickenham
Middlesex TW1 2NL
☎ 081-892 5115

Palladian villa by the Thames, built 1724-9 for Henrietta Howard, mistress of George II, now furnished with paintings and furniture of the period, including works by Hayman, Gravelot, Reynolds, Wilson and Panini.

10.00-16.00 Daily Oct-Maundy Thurs. 10.00-18.00 Daily Good

Fri-30 Sept. Closed Christmas
Eve & Christmas Day.
£ Free
₱
P
A
⊖ Richmond
⇌ St. Margaret's, Richmond
🚌 33, 90, 290, H22, R68, R70

Name of Governing Body:
English Heritage
Nationally funded

Marianne North Gallery

Royal Botanic Gardens
Richmond
Kew
Surrey TW9 3AB
☎ 081-940 1171

Collection of flower paintings
by Marianne North.

Telephone for current opening
times
£ Subject to review,
Concessions
₱
✗
P
S
⊖ Kew Gardens
⇌ Kew Gardens, Kew Bridge
🚌 65, 391

Name of Governing Body:
**Trustees of the Royal Botanic
Gardens, Kew**
National

MCC Museum

Lord's Ground
St John's Wood
London NW8 8QN
☎ 071-289 1611 Curator
☎ 071-266 3825 Tours Dept

The history of cricket from 1550
to the present day comes to life
on a tour of the Long Room and
Museum containing portraits of
the famous, bats used by the
great stroke players, video
highlights of outstanding
matches, and the Ashes.

10.30-17.00 Mon-Sat
matchdays, 12.00-17.00 Sun
matchdays for ticket holders.
Tours normally at 12.00 &
14.00 daily except Test
matches, Cup Finals and
preparation days. Advance
booking desirable.
£ + Museum only on
matchdays, +++ tours on non-
match days.
✗ G
⊖ St John's Wood, Marylebone
⇌ Marylebone
🚌 13, 82, 113, 139, 274

Name of Governing Body:
Marylebone Cricket Club
Independent

Metropolitan Police Thames Division Museum

TDHQ
Wapping Police Station
98 Wapping High Street
London E1 9NE
☎ 071-488 5391

Collection of a wide variety of
material relating to the history
of the Thames Division, the river
police.

Open by written appointment
£ Free
⊖ Tower Hill, Wapping
🚌 100

Name of Governing Body:
**Metropolitan Police Museum
Trust**
Independent

Metropolitan Police Traffic Museum

Catford TDP
34 Aitken Road
Catford
London SE6 3BG
☎ 081-461 0099

Collection includes motorcycles
and police cars and may be
visited as part of a tour of the
traffic garage.

37

Open by appointment
£ Free
P
≷ Bellingham
🚍 36, 36B, 47, 54, 124, 172, 180, 181, 208, 284

Name of Governing Body:
Metropolitan Police Museum Trust
Independent

Michael Faraday's Laboratory and Museum (Royal Institution)

Royal Institution of Great Britain
21 Albemarle Street
London W1X 4BS
☎ 071-409 2992

Historic scientific apparatus, manuscripts and Faraday personalia.

13.00-16.00 Mon-Fri, except Public Hols. Parties by appointment.
£ +
X G
⊖ Green Park
🚍 9, 14, 19, 22, 38

Name of Governing Body:
The Royal Institution of Great Britain
Independent

Museum of Artillery in the Rotunda

Repository Road
Woolwich
London SE18
☎ 081-781 3127
☎ 081-316 5402

Traces the development of the gun from medieval days until the present time. Display housed in an early C19th 'tent' designed by John Nash.

12.00-17.00 Mon-Fri, 13.00-17.00 Sat, Sun, Public Hols. Winter closing 16.00
£ Free
V
P
X G
≷ Woolwich Arsenal, Woolwich Dockyard
🚍 53, 54, 380

Name of Governing Body:
Royal Artillery Institution
Independent

Museum of Fulham Palace

Fulham Palace
Bishops Avenue
London SW6 6EA
☎ 071-736 3233

New museum based in two restored rooms in the former residence of the Bishop of London. Mixed displays including archaeology, paintings and stained glass.

14.00-17.00 Wed-Sun Mar-Oct.
13.00-16.00 Wed-Sun Nov-Feb.
Group tours with refreshments by appointment. Grounds and herb garden open daily.
£ + Concessions
P
⊖ Putney Bridge
≷ Putney
🚍 14, 22, 74, 85, 93, 220, 265, C4

Name of Governing Body:
Fulham Palace Trust
Independent

Museum of Garden History

The Tradescant Trust
Lambeth Palace Road
London SE17 7JU
☎ 071-261 1891

History of the Tradescants, father and son, pre-eminent C17th gardeners, and garden history in general plus changing exhibitions and lectures.

Museum of Fulham Palace

11.00-15.00 Mon-Fri, 10.30-17.00 Sun. Closed Sats.
£ Free
🍵
X G
⊖ Victoria, Waterloo
⇌ Victoria, Waterloo
🚌 3, 77, 159, 344, 507, C10

Name of Governing Body:
The Tradescant Trust
Independent

Museum of London

London Wall
London EC2Y 5HN
☎ 071-600 3699

The story of London and Londoners from prehistory to the present day.

10.00-18.00 Tues-Sat & Bank Hols. 12.00-18.00 Sun.
£ ++ Concessions
✕
W E G
⊖ Barbican, St Paul's, Moorgate
⇌ Moorgate, St Paul's Thameslink
🚌 4, 8, 9, 11, 22B, 25, 141, 279A, 501

Name of Governing Body:
Board of Governors of the Museum of London
Local Authority/Centrally funded

Museum of Mankind

(The Ethnography Dept of the British Museum)
6 Burlington Gardens
London W1X 2EX
☎ 071-437 2224
☎ 071-323 8043 Information

Changing exhibitions illustrating the variety of non-Western cultures. These include the indigenous peoples of Africa, Australia and the Pacific Islands, North and South America and certain parts of Asia and Europe.

10.00-17.00 Mon-Sat. 14.30-18.00 Sun.
£ Free
🍵
X G
⊖ Green Park, Piccadilly Circus, Oxford Circus
🚌 3, 6, 9, 12, 13, 14, 15, 19, 22, 38, 53, 88, 94, 159

Name of Governing Body:
British Museum
National

Museum of Methodism

see Wesley's Chapel and House

Museum of Richmond

Old Town Hall
Whittaker Avenue
Richmond
Surrey TW9 1TP
☎ 081-332 1141

History of the area of Richmond, Kew, Petersham and Ham.

11.00-17.00 Tues-Sat; also Sun 13.30-16.00 May-Oct.
£ + Concessions
W
⊖ Richmond
⇌ Richmond
🚌 27, 33, 65, 190, 337, 391, R61, R69

Name of Governing Body:
The Museum of Richmond
Independent

Museum of the Honourable Artillery Company

Armoury House
City Road
London EC1Y 2BQ
☎ 071-606 4644

History of the Company from the C16th including uniforms, weapons, equipment, applied art, silver and medals.

Open by appointment only
£ Free
⊖ Old St, Moorgate
⇌ Moorgate, Liverpool St
🚌 21, 43, 76, 133, 141, 214, 271, X43

Name of Governing Body:
Honourable Artillery Company
Independent

39

Museum of the Order of St John

St John's Gate
St John's Lane
London EC1M 4DA
☎ 071-253 6644

History of the Order of St John from its foundation during the crusades and of the St John Ambulance service. C16th gatehouse and Norman crypt.

10.00-17.00 Mon-Fri, 10.00-16.00 Sat. Closed Suns and Bank Hols. Tours of Buildings: 11.00 and 14.30 Tues,Fri,Sat.
£ Free
S
⊖ Farringdon
⇌ King's Cross, Farringdon
🚌 55, 56, 153, 243, 279, 505

Name of Governing Body:
The Order of St John
Independent

Museum of the Moving Image

South Bank
Waterloo
London SE1 8XT
☎ 071-928 3535
☎ 071-401 2636 Recorded info

Exciting, informative and fun, the museum traces the story of the moving image from early Chinese Shadow Theatre to film and television technology, with plenty of hands-on involvement. There are also regular changing exhibitions each year.

10.00-18.00 Daily. Last admission one hour before closing. Closed 24-26 Dec inclusive.
£ +++ Concessions
☕
 ✗
W
⊖ Waterloo, Embankment
⇌ Waterloo
🚌 1, 4, 26, 68, 76, 77, 168, 171, 171A, 176, 188, 501, 505, 507, 511, 521, D1, P11

Name of Governing Body:
British Film Institute
National

Museum of the Royal Pharmaceutical Society of Great Britain

1 Lambeth High Street
London SE1 7JN
☎ 071-735 9141

History of pharmacy housed in the headquarters of the Royal Pharmaceutical Society of Great Britain.

09.00-17.00 Mon-Fri, by appointment only
£ Free
A G
⊖ Vauxhall, Westminster, Waterloo
⇌ Vauxhall, Waterloo
🚌 3, 77, 159, 344, 507, C10

Name of Governing Body:
Royal Pharmaceutical Society of Great Britain
Independent

Museum of Zoology and Comparative Anatomy

Biology Department
(Medawar Building)
University College
Gower Street
London WC1E 6BT
☎ 071-387 7050 ext 3564

A teaching and research collection of zoological and palaeontological materials of historic and scientific interest.

09.30-17.00 Mon-Fri, closed Bank Hols and for a week at Easter and Christmas. By appointment only.
£ Free
S
⊖ Euston Sq, Euston, Goodge St, Warren St
⇌ Euston
🚌 10, 14, 14A, 24, 29, 73, 134

Name of Governing Body:
University College London
University

Museum on the Move

Unit C14
Poplar Business Park
10 Preston's Road
London E14 9RL
☎ 071-515 1162

A mobile 'classroom' carrying a wide variety of material designed to convey the history of Docklands to local schools and communities. Part of the service provided by the Museum in Docklands.

£ Free
X

Name of Governing Body:
Board of Governors of the Museum of London
Local Authority/Centrally Funded

Musical Museum

368 High Street
Brentford
Middlesex TW8 OBD
☎ 081-560 8108

An extensive collection of working automatic musical instruments, including everything from a small musical box, fine re-enacting player pianos and a mighty Wurlitzer theatre organ, all regularly demonstrated.

14.00-17.00 Sat & Sun, Apr-Oct and 14.00-16.00 Wed, Thurs and Fri, Jul and Aug.
£ ++ Concessions
S G
⊖ Gunnersbury, South Ealing
⇌ Kew Bridge
🚌 65, 237, 267

Name of Governing Body:
The Musical Museum
Independent

National Army Museum

Royal Hospital Road
London SW3 4HT
☎ 071-730 0717

Story of the British and Commonwealth soldier from 1485 to the present day. Exhibits include personal relics, weapons, medals, models, equipment, reconstructions and one of the world's finest collections of military costume.

10.00-17.30 Daily
£ Free
☕
W G
⊖ Sloane Sq
⇌ Victoria
🚌 11, 19, 22, 137, 239

Name of Governing Body:
The Council of the National Army Museum
National

10.00-17.00 Mon-Fri, 10.00-
18.00 Sat, 14.00-18.00 Sun
Closed Public Hols
£ Free
S G
⊖ Leicester Sq, Charing Cross
⇌ Charing Cross
🚌 3, 6, 9, 11, 12, 13, 15, 23,
24, 29, 30, 53, 77A, 88, 94,
109, 139, 159, 176, 184, 196

National Gallery

Trafalgar Square
London WC2N 5DN
☎ 071-839 3321

Major collection of Western
European paintings dating from
the C13th to the early C20th,
including works by Botticelli,
Van Eyck, Raphael, Titian,
Rembrandt, Canaletto,
Constable, Turner, Monet and
Renoir.

10.00-18.00 Mon-Sat, 14.00-
18.00 Sun.
£ Free
✗
W E G
⊖ Charing Cross, Leicester Sq
⇌ Charing Cross
🚌 3, 6, 9, 11, 12, 13, 15, 23,
24, 29, 30, 53, 77A, 88, 94,
109, 139, 159, 176, 184, 196

Name of Governing Body:
**Trustees of the National
Gallery**
National

National Maritime Museum

Romney Road
London SE10 9NF
☎ 081-858 4422

Superlative maritime collections
tell the history of Britain and the
sea. The museum includes
models of ships of all ages, full
size vessels and battle paintings.

10.00-18.00 Mon-Sat, 14.00-
18.00 Sun.
£ +++ Concessions
☕
✗
X G
DLR: Island Gardens
Riverbus to Greenwich Pier
⇌ Maze Hill
🚌 177, 180, 188, 199, 286

Name of Governing Body:
**Trustees of the National
Maritime Museum**
National

National Portrait Gallery

St Martin's Place
London WC2H OHE
☎ 071-306 0055

Famous British faces from the
Tudors to the present day,
including paintings, sculpture,
etchings, photographs,
miniatures and video films.
There is a daily programme of
slide lectures, room talks and
films for the general public.

Name of Governing Body:
**Trustees of the National
Portrait Gallery**
National

National Postal Museum

King Edward Building
King Edward Street
London EC1A 1LP
☎ 071-239 5420

Postage stamps of the world and the R.M. Phillips Victorian Collection (Penny Blacks, etc)

09.30-16.30 Mon-Fri. Closed weekends and Public Hols.
£ Free
A G
⊖ St Paul's, Barbican
⇌ Moorgate
🚌 4, 8, 22B, 25, 172, 501

Name of Governing Body:
Royal Mail
Independent

Natural History Museum

(incorporating the Geological Museum)
Cromwell Road
London SW7 5BD
☎ 071-938 9123

National collections of living and fossil plants, animals, minerals, rocks and meteorites - a grand total of over 60 million specimens. Inside this fine London landmark, there are hundreds of exciting, interactive exhibits telling the story of life on Earth - from spectacular dinosaurs and fabulous gems, to a blue whale the length of a swimming pool.

10.00-18.00 Mon-Sat, 11.00-18.00 Sun
£ +++ Concessions
Ⓥ
☕

✗
G W
⊖ South Kensington
🚌 14, 49, 74, 349, C1

Name of Governing Body:
Trustees of the Natural History Museum
National

Normansfield Hospital Theatre

Normansfield Hospital
Kingston Road
Teddington
Middlesex TW11 9JH
☎ 081-977 7583

Important listed C19th entertainment theatre in working condition.

Open by appointment only
£ Free
Ⓟ
⇌ Hampton Wick
🚌 281, 285

Name of Governing Body:
Normansfield Hospital
Independent

North Woolwich Old Station Museum

Pier Road
North Woolwich
London E16 2JJ
☎ 071-474 7244

The Victorian station by the Woolwich Ferry has indoor and outdoor exhibits including engines and a re-constructed ticket office, which tell the story of the Great Eastern Railway and the impact of railways on east London's suburbs.

Reference collections of local railway material can be studied by appointment.

10.00-17.00 Mon, Tues, Wed.
10.00-17.00 Sun and Bank Hols.
£ Free
X G
⇌ North Woolwich
🚌 69, 101, 276

Name of Governing Body:
Governors of the Passmore Edwards Museum
Local Authority

Odontological Museum

The Royal College of Surgeons
35-43 Lincoln's Inn Fields
London WC2A 3PN
☎ 071-405 3474 ext 3020

Collections relating to the scientific study of teeth, skulls and the history of dentistry.

10.00-17.00 Mon-Fri by appointment for members of medical and dental professions, students and researchers.
£ Free
A
⊖ Holborn, Temple
🚌 1, 8, 22B, 25, 68, 168, 171, 188, 501, 505, 521

Name of Governing Body:
The Royal College of Surgeons of England
Independent

Old Operating Theatre Museum & Herb Garret

9a St Thomas' Street
Southwark
London SE1 9RT
☎ 071-955 4791

Sole surviving example in England of an early C19th operating theatre with exhibits on the history of surgery, nursing, herbal medicine, St Thomas' and Guy's Hospitals.

12.30-16.00 Mon, Wed and Fri and the first Sunday of each month.
£ + Concessions
S
⊖ London Bridge
⇌ London Bridge
🚌 17, 21, 22A, 35, 40, 43, 47, 48, 133, 214, 344, 501, 505, D1, D11, P3, P11

Name of Governing Body:
Lord Brock's Trust
Independent

Old Royal Observatory, Greenwich

Enquiries to National Maritime Museum
☎ 081-858 4422

The original home of Greenwich Mean Time, the observatory houses the largest refracting telescope in the U.K. and a collection of historic time pieces and navigational instruments.

10.00-18.00 Mon-Sat, 12.00-18.00 Sun, Apr-Sept. 10.00-17.00 Mon-Sat, 14.00-17.00 Sun, Oct-Mar.
£ +++ Concessions
S
DLR: Island Gardens
Cruises from Westminster, Charing Cross
River Bus to Greenwich Pier
⇌ Maze Hill
🚌 53

Name of Governing Body:
Trustees of the National Maritime Museum
National

Oriental and India Office Collections

197 Blackfriars Road
London SE1 8NG
☎ 071-412 7873

One of the oldest research institutions, originating in the records of the East India Company plus the British Library's oriental manuscripts and printed books. Major painting, drawing and manuscript collections relating to the whole of Asia and Islamic North Africa.

09.30-17.45 Mon-Fri, 09.30-12.45 Sat
£ Free
Ⓥ
⊖ Waterloo, Blackfriars
⇌ Waterloo
🚌 1, 4, 26, 45, 59, 63, 68, 76, 77, 149, 168, 171, 176, 188, 501, 505, 507, D1, P11

Name of Governing Body:
British Library
National

Orleans House Gallery

Riverside
Twickenham
Middlesex TW1 3DJ
☎ 081-892 0221

Early C18th baroque Octagon and adjacent gallery holding temporary exhibitions, including local topography, Ionides and Richmond-upon-Thames Art Collections C18th-C20th.

13.00-17.30 Tues-Sat, 14.00-17.30 Sun & Bank Hols, Apr-Sept. Closes at 16.30, Oct-Mar.
£ Free
Ⓟ
X G
⊖ Richmond
⇌ St Margaret's, Twickenham
🚌 33, 90, 290, H22, R68, R70

Name of Governing Body:
London Borough of Richmond-upon-Thames
Local Authority

Osterley Park House

Osterley
Middlesex TW7 4RB
☎ 081-560 3918

Set in 140 acres of landscaped park, Osterley is one of the last great houses with an intact estate in Greater London. The superb interiors conjure up a vivid picture of how the well-to-do lived in the eighteenth century.

13.00-17.00 Wed-Sat, 11.00-17.00 Sun & Bank Hols Apr-Oct. Closed Good Friday.

£ ++ Concessions
🍵
🅿
A G
⊖ Osterley
🚌 H91

Name of Governing Body:
National Trust
Independent

Passmore Edwards Museum

Romford Road
Stratford
London E15 4LZ
☎ 081-534 2274/0276

Archaeology, local history and natural history displays include examples of the famous Bow porcelain as well as putting the London Borough of Newham into its east London and Essex contexts. Recently refurbished.

11.00-17.00 Wed-Fri, 14.00-17.00 Sat and Sun.
£ Free
X G
⊖ Stratford
🚄 Stratford
🚌 25, 86, 104, 108, 147, 158, 238, S2

Name of Governing Body:
Governors of the Passmore Edwards Museum
Local Authority

Percival David Foundation of Chinese Art

53 Gordon Square
London WC1H OPD
☎ 071-387 3909

Collection of Chinese ceramics, C10th to C18th.

10.30-17.00 Mon-Fri.
£ Free
A G
⊖ Russell Sq, Euston Sq, Goodge St
🚄 Euston
🚌 10, 14, 14A, 18, 24, 29, 73, 134

Name of Governing Body:
School of Oriental & African Studies, University of London
University

Petrie Museum of Egyptian Archaeology

University College London
Gower Street
London WC1E 6BT
☎ 071-387 7050 ext 2884

Large collection of Ancient Egyptian antiquities derived chiefly from the excavations of W.M. Flinders Petrie, his colleagues and successors from 1884 to the present day.

10.00-12.00, 13.15-17.00 Mon-Fri. Closed Christmas and Easter weeks, 4 weeks in summer.
£ Free
A S
⊖ Russell Sq, Goodge St, Warren St
🚄 Euston
🚌 10, 18, 24, 29, 68, 73, 134

Name of Governing Body:
University College London
University

Pitshanger Manor Museum

Mattock Lane
Ealing
London W5 5EQ
☎ 081-567 1227
☎ 081-579 2424 ext 42683

Set in an attractive park, Pitshanger Manor was built by the architect John Soane (1753-1837) as his family home. Furnished period rooms and an extensive display of Martinware pottery and a Martinware fountain.

10.00-17.00 Tues-Sat.
£ Free
Ⓥ
A G
⊖ Ealing Broadway
⇌ Ealing Broadway
🚌 65, 83, 112, 297, E1, E2, E7, E8, E9

Name of Governing Body:
London Borough of Ealing
Local Authority

Polish Institute and Sikorski Museum

20 Prince's Gate
London SW7 1PT
☎ 071-589 9249

Polish militaria, Polish art, historical archives and a library.

14.00-16.00 Mon-Fri. 10.00-16.00 1st Sat of each month.
£ Free
⊖ South Kensington, Knightsbridge
🚌 9, 10, 52

Name of Governing Body:
The Polish Institute
Independent

Pollock's Toy Museum

1 Scala Street
London W1P 1LT
☎ 071-636 3452

Toy theatres, dolls, teddy bears, optical and constructional toys, dolls' houses, miniatures, folk-toys and British made toys.

10.00-17.00 Mon-Sat. Closed Bank Hols.
£ ++ Concessions
S G
⊖ Goodge St
⇌ Euston
🚌 14, 14A, 24, 29, 73, 134

Name of Governing Body:
Trustees of Pollock's Toy Museum
Independent

Prince Henry's Room

17 Fleet Street
London EC4Y 1AA
☎ 071-353 7323

A permanent exhibition of Pepysiana which contains contemporary items, prints and paintings depicting the diarist, Samuel Pepys and the London in which he lived.

11.00-14.00 Mon-Sat. Closed Bank Hols.
£ Free
S
⊖ Temple
⇌ Blackfriars
🚌 4, 11, 23, 26, 76, 172, 521

Name of Governing Body:
Corporation of the City of London
Local Authority

Public Record Office Museum

Chancery Lane
London WC2A 1LR
☎ 081-878 3666

Exhibition illustrating people and communities in public records from the Middle Ages to the present day. Also documents from the national archives, ranging from the Domesday Book to WWII RAF records.

09.30-17.00 Mon-Fri, closed weekends and Public Hols.
£ Free
Ⓥ
S G
⊖ Chancery Lane, Temple, Blackfriars
⇌ Blackfriars,
🚌 4, 11, 15, 23, 26, 76, 521

Name of Governing Body:
Lord Chancellor's Department
National

Pumphouse Educational Museum

Lavender Pond Nature Park
Lavender Road
Rotherhithe
London SE16 1DZ
☎ 071-231 2976

Surrounded by a nature park and pond, the museum houses a collection of artefacts found on the Thames foreshore, Peek Frean's ephemera including a replica of Queen Elizabeth's wedding cake and interactive exhibits. It is also host to a programme of changing temporary exhibitions.

10.00-16.00 Tues-Sun, Summer. 10.00-16.00 Mon-Fri, Winter and by special arrangement.
£ ++ Concessions
☕
🅿
✆ Rotherhithe, Surrey Quays
🚌 P11, 225

Name of Governing Body:
Pumphouse Educational Trust
Independent

Puppet Centre Trust

Battersea Arts Centre
Lavender Hill
London SW11 5TN
☎ 071-228 5335

Nationally important collection of puppets from all countries and cultures including the work of contemporary British puppet makers.

14.00-18.00 Mon-Fri and at other times by appointment
£ Free
☕ in Arts Centre
W
🚉 Clapham Junction
🚌 35, 39, 45A, 77, 77A, 77C, 156, 170, 239, 295, 344, C3

Name of Governing Body:
The Puppet Centre Trust
Independent

Queen's Gallery

Buckingham Palace
London SW1A 1AA
☎ 071-799 2331 Recorded information

Changing exhibitions, drawn from the huge and diverse Royal Collection of paintings and works of art.

10.30-17.00 Tues-Sat, 14.00-17.00 Sun, 10.30-17.00 Bank Hol Mons.

£ ++ Concessions
S G
✆ Victoria, St James's Park, Green Park
🚉 Victoria
🚌 2A, 2B, 8, 11, 14, 16, 19, 22, 24, 36B, 38, 52, 73, 74, 82, 137, 185, 239, 507, 511, C1, C10

Name of Governing Body:
The Royal Collection Department
National

Queen's House

Romney Road
Greenwich
London SE10 9NF
☎ 081-858 4422

C17th palace designed by Inigo Jones for Henrietta Maria, wife of Charles I.

10.00-18.00 Mon-Sat, 12.00-18.00 Sun, Apr-Sept. 10.00-17.00 Mon-Sat, 14.00-17.00 Sun Oct-Mar.
£ +++ Concessions
☕
E
DLR: Island Gardens
Cruises from Westminster, Charing Cross
River Bus to Greenwich Pier
🚉 Maze Hill
🚌 177, 180, 188, 199, 286

Name of Governing Body:
Trustees of the National Maritime Museum
National

Ragged School Museum

46-48 Copperfield Road
Bow
London E3 4RR
☎ 081-980 6405

Late Victorian canalside warehouses converted for use as Ragged School by Dr Barnardo. Collection relating to local history, industry and life in East End. Victorian lessons are available to pre-booked groups in the reconstructed classroom.

10.00-17.00 Wed, Thurs, 14.00-17.00 first Sunday of each month.
£ Free

S
⊖ Mile End
🚌 25, 277, D4, D5, D6, D7

Name of Governing Body:
Ragged School Museum Trust
Independent

Rangers House

Chesterfield Walk
Blackheath
London SE10 8QX
☎ 081-853 0035

Early C18th red brick villa, containing the Suffolk Collection of portraits, which

includes major works by William Larkin, Lely and Kneller. The Dolmetsch Collection of musical instruments on loan from the Horniman Museum.

10.00-16.00 Oct-Maundy Thurs, 10.00-18.00 Good Friday-30 Sept. Closed Christmas Eve and Christmas Day.
£ ++
A
⊖ New Cross (then bus)
⇌ Blackheath
🚌 53, 53X

Name of Governing Body:
English Heritage
Nationally funded

Riesco Collection of Chinese Ceramics

Fairfield Halls
Park Lane
Croydon
Surrey CR9 1DG
☎ 081-681 0821

The collection spans over 2000 years, from early stoneware to C18th Imperial Court porcelain.

10.00-22.00 Daily
£ Free

✗
⇌ East Croydon, West Croydon, South Croydon
🚌 68

Name of Governing Body:
London Borough of Croydon
Local Authority

Royal Academy of Arts

Burlington House
London W1V ODS
☎ 071-439 7438

Permanent collection of works of art by Royal Academicians. Major temporary exhibitions programme.

10.00-18.00 Daily
£ +++ Concessions
✗
W E G
⊖ Green Park, Piccadilly Circus
🚌 9, 14, 22, 38, 55

Name of Governing Body:
President and Council of the Royal Academy of Arts
Independent

Royal Air Force Museum

Grahame Park Way
Hendon
London NW9 5LL
☎ 081-205 2266

One of the world's greatest collections of historic aircraft, including the legendary Hurricane, Vulcan, Lancaster, Gladiator and Biggles' Sopwith Camel. Also exciting flight simulator.

Name of Governing Body:
Trustees of the Royal Armouries
National

Royal Artillery Regimental Museum

Old Royal Military Academy
London SE18 4DN
☎ 081-781 5628

The story of the Royal Regiment of Artillery from its formation in 1716 until today.

12.30-16.30 Mon-Fri
£ Free
S
⇌ Woolwich Arsenal
🚌 122, 161, 161A, 178, 380, 469

Name of Governing Body:
Royal Artillery Institution
Independent

Royal Ballet School Archive

White Lodge
Richmond Park
Surrey TW10 5HR
☎ 081-748 7306

History of ballet and ballet dancers.

Open to researchers by written appointment
£ Free
⇌ Mortlake
🚌 74, 85, 170, 265, K6

Name of Governing Body:
Governors of the Royal Ballet School
Independent

10.00-18.00 Daily
£ +++ Concessions
✗
🅿
W G
⊖ Colindale
⇌ Mill Hill
🚌 32, 204, 292, 303

Name of Governing Body:
Trustees of the RAF Museum
National

Royal Armouries

HM Tower of London
London EC3N 4AB
☎ 071-480 6358

National museum of arms and armour with exhibits from the Dark Ages to the C20th including sporting armours of Henry VIII and Charles I.

09.30-18.00 Mon-Sat & Bank Hols, 14.00-18.00 Sun, Mar-Oct. 09.30-16.00 Mon-Sat, 10.00-17.45 Sun, Nov-Feb.
£ +++ Concessions
X S
⊖ Tower Hill

⇌ London Bridge, Fenchurch St
🚌 15, 42, 78, 100, D1, D9, D11

49

Royal College of Music – Department of Portraits

Prince Consort Road
London SW7 2BS
☎ 071-589 3643

A uniquely comprehensive collection of portraits of musicians as well as the largest archive of concert programmes in Great Britain.

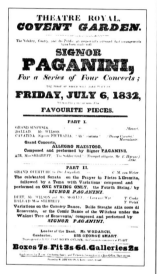

10.00-17.00 Mon-Fri by appointment
£ Free
S G
⊖ South Kensington
🚍 9, 9A, 10, 49, 52, C1

Name of Governing Body:
Royal College of Music
Independent

Royal College of Music – Museum of Instruments

Prince Consort Road
London SW7 2BS
☎ 071-589 3643 ext 4340

An important collection of nearly 600 keyboard, stringed and wind instruments, c.1480 to 1980, mostly European, with some Asian and African examples, including the Tagore, Donaldson, Hipkins, Ridley and Hartley collections.

14.00-16.30 Wed during term-time. Parties and special visits by appointment.
£ + Concessions
S G

⊖ South Kensington
🚍 9, 9A, 10, 49, 52, C1

Name of Governing Body:
Royal College of Music
Independent

Royal College of Obstetricians

27 Sussex Place
Regent's Park
London NW1 4RG
☎ 071-262 5425 ext 213

Obstetrical and gynaecological instruments and the Chamberlen forceps, a collection of midwifery instruments dating from the C16th.

Open by appointment
£ Free
⊖ Baker St
⇌ Marylebone
🚍 13, 82, 113, 139, 274

Name of Governing Body:
Royal College of Obstetricians & Gynaecologists
Independent

Royal College of Physicians

11 St Andrew's Place
Regent's Park
London NW1 4LE
☎ 071-935 1174 ext 374

Around 350 paintings, busts, medals and miniatures from the C16th to C20th, mostly portraits of medical and scientific personalities.

10.00-17.00 Mon-Fri
£ Free

Royal College of Physicians

🖵

⊖ Regent's Park, Great Portland St
⇌ Euston
🚍 18, 27, 135, C2

Name of Governing Body:
Royal College of Physicians
Independent

Royal Fusiliers Museum

H.M. Tower of London
London EC3N 4AB
☎ 071-480 6082

Artefacts and narratives illustrating the history of the Royal Fusiliers from their foundation in 1685 to the present day.

09.30-16.00 Mon-Sat, Nov-Feb.
09.30-17.45 Mon-Sat, 09.30-16.00 Sun, Mar-Oct.
£ +++ Concessions (for Tower)
+ for Fusiliers Museum
⊖ Tower Hill
⇌ Fenchurch St, London Bridge
🚍 15, 42, 78, 100, 188, D1, D9, D11

Name of Governing Body:
The Trustees of the Royal Fusiliers Museum
Independent

Royal Hospital Chelsea

Royal Hospital Road
Chelsea
London SW3 4SL
☎ 071-730 0161 ext 203

Founded in 1682 as a retreat for veterans of the regular army. Small collection of objects related to the history of the hospital and a medal collection.

10.00-12.00 & 14.00-16.00 Mon-Sat. 14.00-16.00 Suns Apr-Sept.
£ Free
A
⊖ Sloane Sq
⇌ Victoria, Charing Cross
🚍 11, 19, 22,137, 219, 239, C1

Name of Governing Body:
Commissioners of the Royal Hospital
Independent

Royal London Hospital Museum & Archives Centre

St Augustine with St Philip's Church
Newark Street
London E1 2AA
☎ 071-377 7000 ext 3364

Converted crypt containing displays on the history of The Royal London Hospital, including its important contributions to medicine, nursing and dentistry and extensive services to the East End community.

10.00-16.30 Mon-Fri. Closed
Public Hols.
£ Free

X G
⊖ Whitechapel
⇌ Bethnal Green
🚌 25, 253

Name of Governing Body:
The Royal London NHS Trust
Independent

Royal Military School of Music

Kneller Hall
Kneller Road
Twickenham
Middlesex TW2 7DU
☎ 081-898 5533

Wind and stringed instruments
of the C17th onwards as used
in military bands.

Open by appointment
£ Free
⇌ Twickenham, Whitton
🚌 281

Name of Governing Body:
**Board of Trustees of the
Royal Military School of
Music**
Independent

Royal Opera House Archives

Royal Opera House
Floral Street
Covent Garden
London WC2
☎ 071-240 1200 ext 353

Material documenting the
history of the Royal Opera

House including photographs,
prints, plans and playbills.

10.30-13.00 & 14.30-17.30
Mon, Tues, Thurs, Fri, by
appointment only. Foyer
displays open to theatregoers.
£ Free
⊖ Covent Garden
⇌ Charing Cross
🚌 1, 4, 6, 9, 11, 13, 15, X15,
68, X68, 77A, 168, 171, 171A,
176, 177, 188, 196, 501, 505

Name of Governing Body:
Royal Opera House Company
Independent

Rugby Museum

Rugby Football Union
Twickenham
Middlesex TW1 1DZ
☎ 081-892 8161

Conducted behind-the-scenes
tours include the grounds,
changing rooms and famous
baths. Displays include Rugby
videos and material
commemorating over 150 years
of the game.

Pre-booked tours 10.30 &
14.15 Mon-Fri.
£ Free
P

⊖ Hounslow East then bus
⇌ Twickenham
🚍 281

Name of Governing Body:
Rugby Football Union
Independent

aatchi Collection

98a Boundary Road
London NW8 0RH
☎ 071-624 8299

Contemporary collection
founded in 1970 containing
works from America, Europe
and Britain by artists such as
Andy Warhol, Paula Rego and
Lucian Freud.

12.00-18.00 Fri & Sat
£ Free
5 G
⊖ St John's Wood, Swiss
Cottage
⇌ South Hampstead
🚍 31, 139

Name of Governing Body:
Privately owned
Independent

St Bartholomew's Hospital Anaesthetics Museum

West Smithfield
London EC1A 7BE
☎ 071-601 8888 ext 7518

Large study and teaching
collections including all aspects
of the evolution of anaesthetics.

Open to researchers by
appointment
£ Free
⊖ Barbican, St Paul's
⇌ Moorgate

🚍 4, 8, 22B, 25, 56, 153, 172,
279, 501

Name of Governing Body:
Privately administered
Independent

St Bartholomew's Hospital Archives

West Smithfield
London EC1A 7BE
☎ 071-601 8152

Paintings, silverware, furniture,
archaeological finds from the
hospital site and the hospital
archives.

Open to researchers by
appointment
£ Free
⊖ St Paul's, Barbican
⇌ Moorgate
🚍 4, 8, 22B, 25, 56, 153, 172,
279, 501

Name of Governing Body:
**City & Hackney Health
Authority**
Health Authority

St Bartholomew's Hospital Pathology Museum

West Smithfield
London EC1A 7BE
☎ 071-601 8888 ext 8536

The medical school was the first
to establish a museum in
London. It now contains
watercolours and photographs
of surgical conditions as well as
pathological specimens, and a
surgical instrument collection.

Open to researchers by
appointment

£ Free
⊖ St Paul's, Barbican
⇌ Moorgate
🚍 4, 8, 22B, 25, 56, 153, 172,
279, 501

Name of Governing Body:
**City & Hackney Health
Authority**
Health Authority

St Bernard's Hospital Museum

Uxbridge Road
Southall
Middlesex UB1 3EU
☎ 081-574 2444 ext 5203

Artefacts and records dating
back to the opening of the
hospital in 1831, including
leather restraints and a padded
cell.

09.00-17.00 Mon-Fri by
appointment
£ +
🅿
⊖ Ealing Broadway, Ealing
Common
⇌ Hanwell, Southall, Ealing
Broadway
🚍 83, 92, 195, 207, 607

Name of Governing Body:
Ealing Health Authority
Independent

St Bride's Crypt Exhibition

St Bride's Church
Fleet Street
London EC4Y 8AU
☎ 071-353 1301

Roman pavement and various
architectural remains from the
seven previous churches on this

53

site. Historical display of the development of printing and the City of London.

08.30-17.00 Daily
£ Free
⊖ Blackfriars
⇌ Blackfriars, St Paul's Thameslink
🚌 4, 11, 15, X15, 23, 26, 45, 59, 63, 76, 172, 521

Name of Governing Body:
Rector and Churchwardens
Independent

St Paul's Cathedral

see Diocesan Treasury in the Crypt of St Paul's Cathedral

Salvation Army International Heritage Centre

117-121 Judd Street
King's Cross
London WC1H 9NN
☎ 071-387 1656 exts 256/244

Salvation Army history, 1865 to the present day.

09.30-15.30 Mon-Fri. 09.30-12.30 Sat
£ Free
⊖ King's Cross, Euston
⇌ King's Cross, St Pancras,
🚌 10, 14, 14A, 17, 18, 30, 45, 46, 63, 73, 74, 214, 259, C12

Name of Governing Body:
The Salvation Army
Independent

Science Museum

Exhibition Road
South Kensington
London SW7 2DD
☎ 071-938 8000

Outstanding collections form an unparalleled record of mankind's greatest inventions and achievements. There are nearly a thousand working exhibits with a chance to try out your own experiments in 'Launch Pad', the interactive gallery or test your skill at flying a model jump jet in 'Flight Lab'. Includes the Wellcome Museum of the History of Medicine.

10.00-18.00 Mon-Sat, 11.00-18.00 Sun.
£ +++ Concessions
Ⓥ
🍵
W G
⊖ South Kensington
🚌 9, 9A, 10, 14, 45A, 49, 52, 74, 249, 349, C1, C2

Name of Governing Body:
Trustees of the Science Museum
National

Shakespeare Globe Museum

Bear Gardens
Bankside
Liberty of the Clink
London SE1 9EB
☎ 071-620 0202

Models and illustrations depicting the theatres of Shakespeare's London and a replica C17th stage used for lectures for schools and theatrical workshops. Also an exhibition on the excavation of the Rose Theatre.

10.00-17.00 Mon-Sat, 14.00-17.30 Sun
£ ++ Concessions
Ⓥ
X G
⊖ London Bridge, Cannon St, Mansion House, Waterloo
⇌ London Bridge, Waterloo
🚌 17, 45, 59, 63, 172, 149, 344, P11

Name of Governing Body:
Shakespeare Globe Trust
Independent

Sherlock Holmes Museum

221b Baker Street
London NW1 6XE
☎ 071-935 8866

Restored Victorian lodging house containing Sherlock Holmes memorabilia.

10.00-18.00 Daily
£ +++ Concessions
Tea by arrangement
⊖ Baker Street
⇌ Marylebone
🚍 2A, 2B, 13, 18, 27, 74, 82, 113, 139, 159, 274

Name of Governing Body:
Sherlock Holmes International Society
Independent

Silver Studio Collection

Middlesex University
Bounds Green Road
London N11 2NQ
☎ 081-368 1299 ext 7339

Comprehensive collection of decorative design material documenting the work of the Silver Studio of Design from 1880 until the 1950s.

10.00-16.00 Mon-Fri, appointments appreciated
£ Free
Ⅴ
☕
⊖ Bounds Green
⇌ Bowes Park, New Southgate
🚍 221

Name of Governing Body:
Middlesex University
University

Sir John Soane's Museum

13 Lincoln's Inn Fields
London WC2A 3BP
☎ 071-405 2107
☎ 071-430 0175 Information

Built by Sir John Soane RA in 1812-13 as his private residence. Contains his collection of antiquities, works of art and architectural drawings and library.

10.00-17.00 Tues-Sat, 18.00-21.00 first Tues of each month. Library/archives by appointment.
£ Free
S
⊖ Holborn, Temple
🚍 1, 8, 22B, 25, 68, 98, 168, 171, 188, 501, 505, 521

Name of Governing Body:
Trustees of Sir John Soane's Museum
National

South London Gallery

65 Peckham Road
London SE5 8UH
☎ 071-703 6120

Changing exhibitions of contemporary art throughout the year and permanent collection of paintings and drawings by British artists.

10.00-17.00 Tues, Wed, Fri. 10.00-19.00 Thurs, 14.00-17.00 Sun. Closed Mon, Sat & Bank Hols.
£ Free
S G
⊖ Elephant & Castle, Oval then bus
⇌ Peckham Rye
🚌 12, 36, 36B, 171

Name of Governing Body:
London Borough of Southwark
Local Authority

Springfield Hospital Museum

61 Glenburnie Road
London SW17 7DJ
☎ 081-672 9911

Collection relating to the history of this psychiatric hospital.

Open by appointment
£ Free
🅿
⊖ Tooting Bec
🚌 219, 249, 349, 355, G2

Name of Governing Body:
Springfield Hospital
Independent

Story of Telecommunications

145 Queen Victoria Street
London EC4V 4AT
☎ 071-248 7444
☎ 0800-289 689 Free information line.

BT's prize winning museum tells the story of 200 years of telecommunications history through a series of 'touch and try' displays, videos and exhibits from the historical collection.

10.00-17.00 Mon-Fri.
£ Free
S G
⊖ Blackfriars, St Paul's
⇌ Blackfriars
🚌 45, 59, 63, 172

Name of Governing Body:
British Telecommunications plc
Independent

Strang Print Room

see University College Art Collection

Sutton House

2 & 4 Homerton High Street
Hackney
London E9 6JQ
☎ 081-986 2264

The oldest house in east London, built in 1535. Contains C16th panelling and decorated fireplaces, C17th wall paintings, C18th panelled room and Tudor well. Recently restored by the National Trust. Permanent historic exhibition and contemporary art gallery.

11.30-17.30 Wed & Sun, Bank Hol Mons Feb-Nov. Closed Good Friday. Art Gallery, Shop and Café also open Thurs-Sat.
£ +
☕
W
⇌ Hackney Central, Homerton
🚌 22A, 22B, 30, 38, 48, 55, 106, 253, S2, W15

Name of Governing Body:
National Trust
Independent

Syon House

Syon Park
Brentford
Middlesex TW8 8JF
☎ 081-560 0881

Fine suite of rooms by Robert Adam and an important collection of paintings including works by Gainsborough and Reynolds, Van Dyck and Lely. Ticket includes 'Sound Alive' tour of house.

11.00-17.00 Wed-Sun, Apr-Sept. Closed Mon & Tues except Bank Hols. Also open on Suns in

Oct. Gardens open daily 10.00-18.00 or dusk except Christmas Day and Boxing Day.
£ +++ (Gardens and House) Concessions
£ ++ House only
☕
✕
🅿
X G
⊖ Gunnersbury, then bus
⇌ Kew Bridge then bus
🚌 116, 117, 237, 267

Name of Governing Body:
Privately owned
Independent

Tate Gallery

Millbank
London SW1P 4RG
☎ 071-821 1313
☎ 071-821 7128 Recorded information

National collections of British painting and C20th international painting and sculpture.

10.00-17.50 Mon-Sat. 14.00-17.50 Sun.
£ Free
☕
✕
W E G

⊖ Pimlico
⇌ Vauxhall
🚌 2A, 2B, 36, 36B, 77A, 88, 185, C10

Name of Governing Body:
The Trustees of the Tate Gallery
National

Theatre Museum

Russell Street
Covent Garden
London WC2E 7PA
☎ 071-836 7891

Britain's national museum of the Performing Arts tells the story of theatre from Shakespeare to the present day, in permanent displays and changing exhibitions.

11.00-19.00 Tues-Sun.
£ ++ Concessions
W G E
⊖ Covent Garden
⇌ Charing Cross
🚌 1, 4, 6, 9, 11, 13, 15, 23, 26, 68, 76, 77A, 168, 171, 171A, 176, 188, 501, 505, 521

Name of Governing Body:
Trustees of the Victoria & Albert Museum
National

Thomas Coram Foundation for Children

40 Brunswick Square
London WC1N 1AZ
☎ 071-278 2424

Built on the site of the original Foundling Hospital; contains an important collection of C18th British paintings, musical scores

by Handel and mementoes from the Foundling Hospital.

09.30-16.00 Mon-Fri. Closed Public Hols. Visitors are advised to confirm opening.
£+
A G
⊖ Russell Sq
⇌ King's Cross, St Pancras
🚌 17, 45, 68, 168, 188

Name of Governing Body:
Thomas Coram Foundation for Children
Independent

Tower Bridge

Museum and Bridge
London SE1 2UP
☎ 071-403 3761

A new state-of-the-art exhibition will give an insight into the history, design, function and operation of this unique bridge. Spectacular views of London from high level walkways and original Victorian steam engines.

Tower Bridge will be closed 4 Jan-30 June 1993. Re-opens 1 July 1993. 10.00-18.30 Daily Apr-Oct; 10.00-17.15 Daily Nov-Mar.
£ ++ Concessions
✕
🅿
X G
⊖ Tower Hill, London Bridge
Riverboat to Tower Pier
DLR: Tower Gateway
⇌ London Bridge, Fenchurch St
🚌 15, 42, 78, 100, D1, X15, P11

Name of Governing Body:
Corporation of the City of London
Local Authority

Tower of London

see HM Tower of London

Tower Hill Pageant

Tower Hill
London EC3
☎ 071-709 0081

Ride through 2000 years of history, seeing, hearing and smelling the past in London's first dark-ride museum. Displays include over 1000 Roman and medieval finds.

09.30-17.30 Daily. Closes 16.30 in winter.
£ +++ Concessions
V
▄
✗
X
⊖ Tower Hill
⇌ Fenchurch St, London Bridge
🚌 15, 25, 42, 78, 100, D1, D9, D11

Name of Governing Body:
Culverin Consortium Limited
Independent

Trades Union Congress Collection

Congress House
Great Russell Street
London WC1B 3LS
☎ 071-636 4030

Archives and ephemera relating to the history of the TUC.

Open for research by appointment
£ Free
⊖ Tottenham Court Rd

🚌 7, 8, 10, 14, 14A, 19, 22B, 24, 25, 29, 38, 55, 73, 98, 134, 176

Name of Governing Body:
Trades Union Congress
Independent

Twinings in the Strand

216 Strand
London WC2
☎ 071-353 3511

Collection relating to the history of tea.

09.30-16.00 Mon-Fri (large groups not possible).
£ Free
X
⊖ Temple, Aldwych
⇌ Charing Cross
🚌 1, 4, 6, 9, 11, 13, 15, 23, 26, 76, 77A, 168, 171A, 176, 188, 505, X15, X68

Name of Governing Body:
R. Twining and Company Limited
Independent

University College Art Collection

Strang Print Room
University College
Gower Street
London WC1E 6BT
☎ 071-387 7050

An important collection of fine art including European prints, drawings and paintings, Japanese prints and sculptures by Flaxman. Works are displayed in the Flaxman Gallery and the Strang Print Room.

13.00-14.30 Mon-Fri term-time. Reserve collection open by appointment.
£ Free
⊖ Warren St, Euston Sq, Goodge St, Euston
⇌ Euston
🚌 10, 14, 14A, 24, 29, 73, 134

Name of Governing Body:
University College Art Collections Committee
University

University College Department of Geological Sciences Collection

Dept of Geological Sciences
University College
Gower Street
London WC1E 6BT
☎ 071-387 7050

Teaching and research collection of geological specimens including a print and photograph collection.

Open by appointment
£ Free
▄
⊖ Euston Sq, Goodge St, Warren St, Euston
⇌ Euston
🚌 10, 14, 14A, 24, 29, 73, 134

Name of Governing Body:
University College London
University

Upminster Tithe Barn

Hall Lane
Upminster
Essex RM14 1AU
☎ 0708-447535

Large C15th barn containing collections of agricultural and

domestic items relating to the local area.

14.00-18.00 1st weekend in each month, Apr-Oct
£ Free
P
X G
Θ Upminster
≋ Upminster
🚌 248

Name of Governing Body:
Hornchurch & District Historical Society
Independent

Upminster Windmill

St Mary's Lane
Upminster
Essex RM14 2QL
☎ 0708-44297

Smock windmill of 1801. Conducted tours are held to explain the working of the mill, which is internally intact.

14.00-18.00 3rd weekend each month, Apr-Oct
£ Free
Ⓥ
Θ Upminster
≋ Upminster
🚌 246, 248, 370

Name of Governing Body:
Hornchurch & District Historical Society
Independent

Valence House Museum

Becontree Avenue
Dagenham
Essex RM8 3HT
☎ 081-592 4500 ext 4293

C17th timber-framed manor house standing on a medieval moated site. Permanent display on the history of Barking and Dagenham plus the C17th Fanshawe family portraits. There is also a period style herb garden in the grounds.

10.00-16.00 Tues-Sat
£ Free
P
S
≋ Chadwell Heath
🚌 5, 25, 62, 87, 129, 148, B3, B4

Name of Governing Body:
London Borough of Barking and Dagenham
Local Authority

Vestry House Museum

Vestry Road
Walthamstow
London E17 9NH
☎ 081-509 1917

Waltham Forest's local history museum housed in an early C18th workhouse. Permanent displays on local domestic life, reconstructed Victorian parlour, C19th police cell and the Bremer Car (c.1894).

10.00-13.00 & 14.00-17.30 Mon-Fri. Sats closes at 17.00

£ Free
P
S G
Θ Walthamstow Central
≋ Walthamstow Central
🚌 20, 34, 48, 58, 69, 97A, 212, 215, 230, 275, W11, W15

Name of Governing Body:
London Borough of Waltham Forest
Local Authority

Victoria & Albert Museum

Cromwell Road
London SW7 2RL
☎ 071-938 8500

The national collections of sculpture, furniture, textiles and dress, ceramics and glass, silver, jewellery and metalwork drawn from European and non-Western cultures. The V&A also holds extensive collections of prints, photographs and paintings, including the Constable collection. Changing programme of exciting temporary exhibitions.

10.00-17.50 Mon-Sat. 10.00-17.50 Sun.
£ Free, though visitors are asked to make a voluntary donation.
☕
✗
W E G
Θ South Kensington, Knightsbridge
≋ Victoria
🚌 14, 45A, 49, 74, 249, 349, C1

Name of Governing Body:
Trustees of the Victoria & Albert Museum
National

Vintage Wireless Museum

23 Rosendale Road
West Dulwich
London SE21 8DS
☎ 081-670 3667

Collection of around 1,000
radios and televisions, mostly
1917 to 1940.

Open by appointment
£ Free
⇌ West Dulwich
🚌 3, 115

Name of Governing Body:
**The Vintage Wireless
Company (London)**
Independent

Wallace Collection

Hertford House
Manchester Square
London W1M 6BN
☎ 071-935 0687

Permanent collection of Old
Master paintings, French C18th
furniture, ceramics, goldsmiths'
work, miniatures and sculpture,
European and Oriental arms and
armour.

10.00-17.00 Mon-Sat. 14.00-
17.00 Sun
£ Free
X G
⊖ Marble Arch, Bond St, Baker
St
🚌 2A, 2B, 6, 7, 8, 10, 12, 13,
15, 16A, 23, 73, 74, 82, 88,
113, 135, 137, 139, 159

Name of Governing Body:
**Trustees of the Wallace
Collection**
National

Wandle Industrial Museum

The Vestry Hall Annexe
London Road
Mitcham
Surrey CR4 3UD
☎ 081-648 0127

Industrial history of the Wandle
Valley, with plans to establish a
riverside museum reflecting the
rich heritage of the area.

13.00-16.00 Wed and 14.00-
17.00 first Sun of each month.
Open to schools and groups by
appointment.
£ +
⇌ Mitcham
🚌 118, 127, 200, 270, 280,
355

Name of Governing Body:
**Wandle Industrial Museum
Trust**
Independent

Wandsworth Museum

Disraeli Road
Putney
London SW15 2DR
☎ 081-871 7074

The local history of the London
Borough of Wandsworth
including Balham, Battersea,
Putney, Roehampton, Tooting
and Wandsworth.

13.00-17.00 Mon, Tues, Wed,
Fri and Sat.
£ Free
S G
⊖ East Putney
⇌ Putney
🚌 14, 37, 39, 74, 85, 93, 220,
270, 337

Name of Governing Body:
**London Borough of
Wandsworth**
Local Authority

Wellcome Institute for the History of Medicine

see Centre for Medical Science
and History

Wellcome Museum of Anatomy

The Royal College of Surgeons
35-43 Lincoln's Inn Fields
London WC2A 3PN
☎ 071-405 3474

Collection of anatomical prosections, casts, bones and radiographs.

09.00-17.00 Mon-Fri for members of medical and dental professions, students, researchers and artists by appointment only.
£ Free
A
⊖ Holborn, Temple
🚌 1, 8, 22B, 25, 68, 168, 171, 188, 501, 505, 521

Name of Governing Body:
The Royal College of Surgeons of England
Independent

Wellcome Museum of Pathology

The Royal College of Surgeons
35-43 Lincoln's Inn Fields
London WC2A 3PN
☎ 071-405 3474

Collection of over 2000 pathological specimens.

09.00-17.00 Mon-Fri for members of medical professions, students and researchers by appointment only.
£ Free
A
⊖ Holborn, Temple
🚌 1, 8, 22B, 25, 68, 168, 171, 188, 501, 505, 521

Name of Governing Body:
The Royal College of Surgeons of England
Independent

Wellington Museum

see Apsley House, The Wellington Museum

Wesley's Chapel and House

(incorporating the Museum of Methodism)
49 City Road
London EC1Y 1AU
☎ 071-253 2262

The home of John Wesley from 1779-1791. The Museum of Methodism in the chapel crypt illustrates the history of Methodism from the C18th to the present day.

10.00-16.00 Mon-Sat
£ ++ Concessions
S G
⊖ Old St, Moorgate
≥ Old St, Moorgate
🚌 43, 55, 76, 141, 214, 243, 271, 505

Name of Governing Body:
The Methodist Church
Independent

Westminster Abbey Museum

Westminster Abbey
London SW1P 3PA
☎ 071-222 5152

Collection of funeral and other effigies.

10.30-16.00 Daily
£ ++ Concessions
X G
⊖ Westminster, St James's Park
≥ Victoria
🚌 3, 11, 12, 24, 53, 53X, 77A, 88, 109, 159, 177, 184, 511

Name of Governing Body:
The Dean & Chapter of Westminster
Independent

Westminster Dragoons Museum

Cavalry House
Duke of York's HQ
King's Road
Chelsea
London SW3 4SC

History of the regiment.

Open by appointment
£ Free
⊖ Sloane Sq
≥ Victoria
🚌 11, 19, 22, 137, 137A, 219, C1

Name of Governing Body:
Berkshire & Westminster Dragoons Museum Trust
Independent

Whitehall, Cheam

1 Malden Road
Cheam
Surrey SM3 8QD
☎ 081-643 1236
☎ 081-773 4555

Timber-framed house built c.1500 featuring permanent

displays on medieval Cheam pottery, Nonsuch Palace, Cheam School plus changing exhibitions.

14.00-17.30 Tues-Fri & Sun, 10.00-17.30 Sat, Apr-Sept.
14.00-17.30 Wed,Thurs,Sun & 10.00-17.30 Sat, Oct-Mar.
14.00-17.30 Bank Hol Mons.
£ + Concessions

X G
≋ Cheam
🚌 213, 408, 726

Name of Governing Body:
London Borough of Sutton
Local Authority

Wilkinson Sword Museum

11-13 Brunel Road
Acton
London W3 7UH
☎ 081-749 1061

Collection of swords.

Open by appointment
£ Free
⊖ East Acton
🚌 7, 70, 72

Name of Governing Body:
Wilkinson Sword Ltd
Independent

William Morris Gallery

Lloyd Park
Forest Road
London E17 4PP
☎ 081-527 3782

Large collection of William Morris designs and Morris & Co products including textiles, ceramics, furniture and wallpaper, housed in Morris's childhood home, surrounded by attractive gardens. The Brangwyn Gift of paintings and drawings by the Pre-Raphaelites and their contemporaries, as well as works by Sir Frank Brangwyn himself.

10.00-13.00 & 14.00-17.00 Tues-Sat 10.00-12.00 & 14.00-17.00 First Sun of each month.
£ Free
P
A G
⊖ Walthamstow Central
≋ Walthamstow Central
🚌 34, 97, 97A, 215, 257, 275

Name of Governing Body:
London Borough of Waltham Forest
Local Authority

William Morris Society

Kelmscott House
26 Upper Mall
Hammersmith
London W6 9TA
☎ 081-741 3735

Morris & Co textiles, wallpaper sample books and designs. Also the Albion Press, used by Morris for the Kelmscott Press.

14.00-17.00 Thurs & Sat
£ Free
S G
⊖ Ravenscourt Park
🚌 27, 267, 290, H91

Name of Governing Body:
William Morris Society
Independent

Wimbledon Lawn Tennis Museum

The All England Club
Church Road
London SW19 5AE
☎ 081-946 6131

The history and development of Lawn Tennis from mid-Victorian England to the present day.

11.00-17.00 Tues-Sat, 14.00-17.00 Sun. Closed Mon, Bank Hols and Fri, Sat and Sun prior to the Championships. Also closed the middle Sunday of the Championships.
£ ++ Concessions
📷
🅿 Aug-May only
W G
⊖ Southfields
⇌ Wimbledon
🚌 93, 39, 200

Name of Governing Body:
The All England Lawn Tennis Ground Ltd
Independent

Wimbledon Society Museum

26 Lingfield Road
Wimbledon
London SW19
☎ 081-946 9398

Archaeology, prints and drawings, natural history, ephemera, photographs and artefacts all relating to the Wimbledon area.

14.30-17.00 Sats only, otherwise by appointment.
£ Free
S
⊖ Wimbledon
⇌ Wimbledon
🚌 93, 200

Name of Governing Body:
The Wimbledon Society
Independent

Wimbledon Society Museum

Wimbledon Windmill Museum

Windmill Road
Wimbledon Common
London SW19 5NR
☎ 081-947 2825

The history of windmills and windmilling told in pictures, models and the machinery and tools of the trade.

14.00-17.00 Sat, Sun & Public Hols, Easter to end of Oct. Other times for schools and groups.
£ +
📷 🅿 S G
⊖ Wimbledon, Putney
⇌ Wimbledon, Putney
🚌 39, 77C, 93

Name of Governing Body:
Wimbledon Windmill Museum Trust
Independent

Museum in Docklands

Alexander Fleming Laboratory

St Mary's Hospital Trust
Praed Street
Paddington
London W2 1NY
☎ 071-725 6502

Planned re-construction of Fleming's laboratory in St Mary's Hospital. Due for completion in 1993.

Name of Governing Body:
St Mary's Hospital Trust
Independent

Benjamin Franklin House

c/o The Royal Society of Arts
6-8 John Adam Street
London WC2N 6EZ
☎ 071-839 7717

Planned restoration of 36 Craven Street, only surviving home of Benjamin Franklin, as a museum, library and conference centre. Open by appointment only.

Name of Governing Body:
Friends of Benjamin Franklin House
Independent

Cinema Museum

The Old Fire Station
46 Renfrew Road
Kennington
London SE11 4NA
☎ 071-820 9992

History of cinemas from 1898 to the present day. In storage, but can currently be viewed by appointment.

Name of Governing Body:
Board of Directors of the Cinema Museum
Independent

Crossness Engines Trust

c/o The Secretary
8 Yorkland Avenue
Welling
Kent DA16 2LF
☎ 081-303 6273

Four Victorian pumping engines built by James Watt & Co. 1860s. Occasional Open Days, telephone for details.

Name of Governing Body:
Crossness Engines Trust
Independent

Croydon Airport Society

Airport House
Purley Way
Croydon
Surrey CRO OXZ
☎ 081-770 4750 Enquiries

Building currently being refurbished to house a collection of photographs, ephemera and objects relating to Croydon airport.

Name of Governing Body:
Croydon Airport Society
Independent

Croydon Museum

Central Library
Katharine Street
Croydon CR9 1ET
☎ 081-760 5400

Multi-media collections relevant to Croydon people and their histories, due to open in 1994.

Name of Governing Body:
London Borough of Croydon
Local Authority

Girl Guides Museum

Girl Guides Association
17-19 Buckingham Palace Road
London SW1W OPT
☎ 071-834 6242

Film, photographs, costume and personalia relating to the International Girl Guide movement.

Name of Governing Body:
The Girl Guides Association
Independent

New projects in London

Handel House

25 Brook Street
Mayfair
London W1
c/o Music Management (UK) Ltd
PO Box 1105
London SW1V 2DE
☎ 071-976 6262

The house where Handel lived from 1721, when it was built, until his death in 1759, is currently being restored. The upper three floors will be dedicated to a Handel Museum and a specialist library for Handel scholars.

Name of Governing Body:
Handel House Association Ltd
Independent

Heralds' Museum

College of Arms
Queen Victoria Street
London EC4V 4BT
☎ 071-584 0930
☎ 071-236 9857

The museum, which was housed in the Tower of London, is moving to new accommodation.

Name of Governing Body:
The Trustees of the College of Arms Trust
Independent

Heritage Centre Spitalfields

19 Princelet Street
London E1 6QH
☎ 071-377 6901

Permanent display planned in this resource centre for the study of immigration in the Spitalfields area. Visitors welcome by appointment.

Name of Governing Body:
Heritage Centre Spitalfields Committee
Independent

Hillingdon Museum Service

Uxbridge Central Library
High Street
Uxbridge
Middx UB8 1HD
☎ 0895-250711

Local historical and archaeological material. No permanent public display but open to researchers by appointment.

Name of Governing Body:
London Borough of Hillingdon
Local Authority

House Mill Museum Project

c/o Passmore Edwards Museum Service
The Old Dispensary
30 Romford Road
Stratford
London E15 4BZ
☎ 081-534 2274

Restoration of 1776 House Mill. Visitor centre planned for 1993.

Name of Governing Body:
Passmore Edwards Museum Trust
Independent

Islington Museum Service

c/o Leisure Services Department
345 Holloway Road
London N7 ORS
☎ 071-607 7331 ext 254

Proposed museum of local history and the Sickert Collection of paintings.

Name of Governing Body:
London Borough of Islington
Local Authority

Markfield Beam Engine and Museum

Markfield Road
South Tottenham
London N15 4RB
☎ 081-800 7061
☎ 076-387331

Original compound beam pumping engine, built in 1886 and restored to working order. Telephone for details of open days.

Name of Governing Body:
Markfield Beam Engine and Museum
Independent

Merton Heritage Centre/ Museum

c/o Merton Library Service
Merton Civic Centre
London Road
Morden
Surrey SH4 5DX
☎ 081-545 3770

Planned conversion of part of the basement of a C17th house to form a small heritage centre/museum. Collections of multi-media material relevant to the residents of Merton and in particular Mitcham. Due to open 1993.

Name of Governing Body:
London Borough of Merton
Local Authority

Metropolitan Police Museum

c/o Room 1334
New Scotland Yard
London SW1H OBG
☎ 081-305 2824

The museum is currently seeking a new site, whilst the branches, the Traffic Museum, the Mounted Police Museum and the Thames River Police Museum are open by appointment.

Name of Governing Body:
Metropolitan Police Museum Trust
Independent

Millwall FC Museum

Millwall FC
Bolina Road
London SE16
☎ 071-639 3143

Proposed museum of Millwall Football Club, with reference to the Isle of Dogs, East London and New Cross, Bermondsey and South East London. Opening date planned for late summer 1993.

Name of Governing Body:
Millwall FC Museum Association/Trust
Independent

Museum in Docklands

c/o Unit C14
Poplar Business Park
10 Preston's Road
London E14 9RL
☎ 071-515 1162

London's industrial and commercial history. Open by appointment.

Name of Governing Body:
Board of Governors of the Museum of London
Local Authority/Centrally funded

Museum of Soho

St Anne's Tower
55 Dean Street
London W1V 5HH
☎ 071-439 4303

Permanent collection of local history, archive material and books with temporary displays. Opening planned for 1993.

Name of Governing Body:
Museum of Soho Ltd
Independent

Museum of Women's Art

13A Downshire Hill
London NW3 1NR
☎ 081-435 3728

Project to establish a permanent exhibition and resource centre on the historical development of Women's Art in Britain.

Name of Governing Body:
Board of Trustees of Museum of Women's Art
Independent

National Museum of Cartoon Art

c/o 156 Munster Road
London SW6 5RA
☎ 071-731 1372

Collection of humorous and cartoon art from 1750.

Name of Governing Body:
The Cartoon Art Trust
Independent

Outside Archive/Collection

c/o 213 South Lambeth Road
London SW8 1XR
☎ 071-735 2192

Plans to open a museum to house an international collection of works by untrained artists, working outside the cultural tradition.

Name of Governing Body:
Victor Musgrave Outsider Trust
Independent

Redbridge Museum

Central Library
Clements Road
Ilford IG1 1EA
☎ 081-478 7145

Items relating to the local history of Redbridge and its predecessor authorities. A permanent site is planned, meanwhile some items can be seen on display in the central library.

Name of Governing Body:
London Borough of Redbridge
Local Authority

St Mark's Church

(Silvertown E16)
c/o Passmore Edwards Museum
Service
The Old Dispensary
30 Romford Road
Stratford
London E15 4BZ
☎ 081-534 2274

S.S. Teulon church has been
restored to house a museum
about the surrounding Victorian
dockland suburbs.

Name of Governing Body:
**Governors of the Passmore
Edwards Museum**
Local Authority

Southall Railway Centre

Southall
Middlesex UB2 4PL
enquiries to: 16 Grange Close
Heston
Middlesex TW5 0HW
☎ 081-574 1529

The centre, a former steam and
diesel depot, will house a
railway museum and operate a
passenger service running
through the Brent river park and
many other places of interest.
Scheduled to open during
summer 1993.

Name of Governing Body:
GWR Preservation Group Ltd
Independent

Stephens Collection

Avenue House
East End Road
Finchley
London N3
☎ 081-346 6337 Information

Aim to illustrate the history of
handwriting and to
acknowledge the part played by
Henry Stephens. Due to open
March 1993. Opening hours will
be 14.00-16.30 Tues-Thurs.

Name of Governing Body:
The Finchley Society
Independent

Thames Sailing Barge 'Dawn'

c/o North Woolwich Old Station
Museum
Pier Road
London E16 2JJ
☎ 071-474 7244

A London mooring is planned
for the 'Dawn', which should be
available for educational visits,
functions and trips from spring
1994.

Name of Governing Body:
**Governors of the Passmore
Edwards Museum**
Local Authority

Transport Design and Development Museum

Unit X
Station Avenue
Kew
Surrey TW9 3QA
c/o Michael Wilsdon
41 Burlington Avenue
Kew
Surrey TW9 4DG

Unusual vehicles illustrating
important design and
development principles. Guided
tours available.

Name of Governing Body:
Privately owned
Independent

Whitewebbs Museum of Transport and Industry

Whitewebbs Road
Enfield
Middlesex EN2 9HW
☎ 081-367 1898

Project to restore and convert
the former New River pump
house (built 1898) into a
transport museum to house a
collection of early vehicles.

Name of Governing Body:
**The Enfield and District
Veteran Vehicle Trust**
Independent

National Museum of Cartoon Art

* Museum Projects

1. Barking & Dagenham
Valence House Museum

2. Barnet
Barnet Museum
Church Farm House Museum
London Museum of Jewish Life
Royal Air Force Museum
*Stephens Collection

3. Bexley
Bexley Museum
David Evans Craft Centre of Silk
Erith Museum
*Crossness Engines Trust

4. Brent
Grange Museum of Community
History

5. Bromley
Bethlem Royal Hospital Archives
& Museum
Bromley Museum
Charles Darwin Memorial
Museum
Crystal Palace Museum

6. Camden
British Museum
British Oxygen Company
Museum (Charles King
Collection)
Centre for Medical Science and
History and Wellcome Institute
for the History of Medicine
(Fourth Floor Exhibition)
Dickens House Museum
Fenton House
Freud Museum
Hampstead Museum
Hospital for Sick Children
Hunterian Museum
Iveagh Bequest, Kenwood
Jewish Museum
Keats House
Library & Museum of the United
Grand Lodge of England
Museum of Zoology &
Comparative Anatomy
Odontological Museum
Percival David Foundation of
Chinese Art
Petrie Museum of Egyptian
Archaeology
Pollock's Toy Museum
Royal College of Physicians
Saatchi Collection

Salvation Army International
Heritage Centre
Sir John Soane's Museum
Thomas Coram Foundation for
Children
Trades Union Congress
Collection
University College Art Collection
University College Department
of Geological Sciences
Collection
Wellcome Museum of Anatomy
Wellcome Museum of
Pathology
*Museum of Women's Art

7. City of London
All Hallows by the Tower
Undercroft Museum
Bank of England Museum
Barbican Art Gallery
Chartered Insurance Institute
Museum
Clockmakers' Company
Collection
Diocesan Treasury in the Crypt
of St. Paul's Cathedral
Dr. Johnson's House
Guildhall Art Gallery
Guildhall Library (Print Room)
Museum of London
National Postal Museum
Prince Henry's Room
St. Bartholomew's Hospital
Anaesthetics Museum
St. Bartholomew's Hospital
Archives
St. Bartholomew's Hospital
Pathology Museum
St. Bride's Crypt Exhibition
Story of Telecommunications
Tower Bridge
*Heralds' Museum

8. Croydon
Croydon Natural History &
Scientific Society
Riesco Collection of Chinese
Ceramics
*Croydon Airport Society
Museum

Museums by borough

*Croydon Museum

9. Ealing
Guinness Archives
Pitshanger Manor Museum
St Bernard's Hospital Museum
Wilkinson Sword Museum
*Southall Railway Centre

10. Enfield
Forty Hall Museum
*Whitewebb's Museum of
  Transport and Industry

11. Greenwich
Cutty Sark the Clipper Ship
Fan Museum
Greenwich Borough Museum
Museum of Artillery in the
  Rotunda
National Maritime Museum
Old Royal Observatory
Queen's House
Rangers House
Royal Artillery Regimental
  Museum

12. Hackney
Geffrye Museum
Hackney Museum
Sutton House

13. Hammersmith & Fulham
Museum of Fulham Palace
William Morris Society
*National Museum of Cartoon
  Art

14. Haringey
Bruce Castle Museum
Silver Studio Collection
*Markfield Beam Engine and
  Museum

15. Harrow
Harrow Museum & Heritage
  Centre
Harrow School Old Speech
  Room Gallery

16. Havering
Upminster Tithe Barn
Upminster Windmill

17. Hillingdon
Bayhurst Wood Country Park
Knightscote Farm
*Hillingdon Museum Service

18. Hounslow
Boston Manor House
Chiswick House
Gillette UK Ltd
Gunnersbury Park Museum
Hogarth's House
Kew Bridge Steam Museum
Musical Museum
Osterley Park House
Syon House

19. Islington
Crafts Council
Institute of Ophthalmology
  Visual Sciences Collection
London Canal Museum
Museum of the Honourable
  Artillery Company
Museum of the Order of St John
Wesley's Chapel and House
  (incorporating the Museum of
  Methodism)
*Islington Museum

20. Kensington & Chelsea
British Optical Association
  Foundation Collection
Carlyle's House
Chelsea Physic Garden
Commonwealth Institute
Kensington Palace, State
  Apartments & Royal
  Ceremonial Dress Collection
Leighton House Museum
Linley Sambourne House
London Irish Rifles
National Army Museum
Natural History Museum
  (incorporating the Geological
  Museum)
Polish Institute & Sikorski
  Museum

Royal Hospital Chelsea
Science Museum
Victoria & Albert Museum

21. Kingston-upon-Thames
Frederick W. Paine Museum
Kingston-upon-Thames
  Museum & Heritage Centre

22. Lambeth
Black Cultural Archives/Museum
Florence Nightingale Museum
Museum of Garden History
Museum of the Moving Image
Museum of the Royal
  Pharmaceutical Society of
  Great Britain
Vintage Wireless Museum
*Cinema Museum
*Outsider Archive/Collection

23. Lewisham
Horniman Museum & Gardens
Metropolitan Police Traffic
  Museum

24. Merton
Wandle Industrial Museum
Wimbledon Lawn Tennis
  Museum
Wimbledon Society Museum
Wimbledon Windmill Museum
*Merton Heritage Centre/
  Museum

25. Newham
East Ham Nature Reserve
Museum on the Move
North Woolwich Old Station
  Museum
Passmore Edwards Museum
*House Mill Museum Project
*Museum in Docklands
*St. Mark's Church
*Thames Sailing Barge 'Dawn'

26. Redbridge
*Redbridge Museum

27. Richmond-upon-Thames
Embroiderers' Guild

Ham House
Hampton Court Palace
Kew Collections of Economic
Botany
Kew Gardens Gallery
Kew Palace and Queen
Charlotte's Cottage
Marble Hill House
Marianne North Gallery
Museum of Richmond
Normansfield Hospital Theatre
Orleans House Gallery
Royal Ballet School Archive
Royal Military School of Music
Rugby Museum
*Transport Design and
Development Museum

28. Southwark
Amalgamated Engineering and
Electrical Union Collection
Bankside Gallery
Bramah Tea and Coffee
Museum
Brunel's Engine House
Cuming Museum
Design Museum
Dulwich Picture Gallery
Gordon Museum
Government Art Collection
HMS Belfast
Imperial War Museum
Kirkaldy Testing Museum
Livesey Museum
London Fire Brigade Museum
Old Operating Theatre, Museum
& Herb Garret
Oriental and India Office
Collections
Pumphouse Educational
Museum
Shakespeare Globe Museum
South London Gallery
*Millwall FC Museum

29. Sutton
Carshalton Water Tower
Heritage Centre,
Honeywood
Little Holland House
Whitehall, Cheam

30. Tower Hamlets
Bethnal Green Museum of
Childhood
HM Tower of London
Island History Trust
London Chest Hospital
London Gas Museum
Metropolitan Police Thames
Division Museum
Ragged School Museum
Royal Armouries
Royal Fusiliers Museum
Royal London Hospital Museum
& Archives Centre
Tower Hill Pageant
*Heritage Centre Spitalfields

31. Waltham Forest
Epping Forest Museum & Queen
Elizabeth's Hunting Lodge
Vestry House Museum
William Morris Gallery

32. Wandsworth
Puppet Centre Trust
Springfield Hospital Museum
Wandsworth Museum

33. Westminster
Alfred Dunhill Collection
Apsley House, Wellington
Museum
Arts Council Collection
Baden-Powell House
Ben Uri Art Society
British Architectural Library
Drawings Collection & RIBA
Heinz Gallery
British Council Collection

British Dental Association
Museum
Cabinet War Rooms
Courtauld Institute Galleries
Czech Memorial Scrolls Centre
Guards Museum
Inns of Court & City Yeomanry
Museum
London Scottish Regimental
Museum
London Toy & Model Museum
London Transport Museum
MCC Museum
Michael Faraday's Laboratory &
Museum (Royal Institution)
Museum of Mankind
National Gallery
National Portrait Gallery
Public Record Office Museum
Queen's Gallery
Royal Academy of Arts
Royal College of Music -
Department of Portraits
Royal College of Music -
Museum of Instruments
Royal College of Obstetricians
Royal Opera House Archives
Sherlock Holmes Museum
Tate Gallery
Theatre Museum
Twinings in the Strand
Wallace Collection
Westminster Abbey Museum
Westminster Dragoons Museum
*Alexander Fleming Laboratory
*Benjamin Franklin House
*Girl Guides Museum
*Handel House
*Metropolitan Police Museum
*Museum of Soho

Cutty Sark the Clipper Ship

National Portrait Gallery

Agricultural History
Bexley Museum
Knightscote Farm
Upminster Tithe Barn
Upminster Windmill
Wimbledon Windmill Museum

Archaeology
All Hallows by the Tower
  Undercroft Museum
Barnet Museum
Bexley Museum
British Museum
Bromley Museum
Carshalton Water Tower
Croydon Natural History &
  Scientific Society
Cuming Museum
Erith Museum

Freud Museum
Greenwich Borough Museum
Gunnersbury Park Museum
Harrow School Old Speech
  Room Gallery
Kingston-upon-Thames
  Museum & Heritage Centre
Museum of London
Passmore Edwards Museum
Petrie Museum of Egyptian
  Archaeology
Pumphouse Educational
  Museum
St Bartholomew's Hospital
  Archives
St Bride's Crypt Museum
Sir John Soane's Museum
Tower Hill Pageant
Whitehall, Cheam
Wimbledon Society Museum

Ceramics
Bramah Tea and Coffee
  Museum
British Museum
Crafts Council
Cuming Museum
Fenton House
Leighton House Museum
Library & Museum of the United
  Grand Lodge of England
Museum of the Royal
  Pharmaceutical Society of
  Great Britain
Percival David Foundation of
  Chinese Art
Petrie Museum of Egyptian
  Archaeology
Pitshanger Manor Museum
Riesco Collection of Chinese
  Ceramics
Victoria & Albert Museum
Wallace Collection
Whitehall, Cheam
William Morris Gallery

Clocks & Watches
British Museum
Clockmakers' Company
  Collection
Library & Museum of the United
  Grand Lodge of England
Old Royal Observatory
Victoria & Albert Museum
Wallace Collection

Coins & Banking
Bank of England Museum
Barnet Museum
British Museum

Company History
Alfred Dunhill Collection
Bank of England Museum
David Evans Craft Centre of Silk
Frederick W. Paine Museum
Gillette UK Ltd
Guinness Archives
Kirkaldy Testing Museum

Museums by subject

London Gas Museum
London Transport Museum
National Postal Museum
Oriental and India Office
  Collections
Silver Studio Collection
Story of Telecommunications
Twinings in the Strand
Wilkinson Sword Museum

Contemporary
Arts Council Collection
Design Museum
Embroiderers' Guild
Forty Hall Museum
Geffrye Museum
Grange Museum of Community
  History
Imperial War Museum
London Museum of Jewish Life
Museum of London
Museum of the Moving Image
Puppet Centre Trust
Royal Academy of Arts
Saatchi Collection
Science Museum
Tate Gallery
Victoria & Albert Museum

Costume & Textiles
Barnet Museum
Diocesan Treasury in the Crypt
  of St Paul's Cathedral
Embroiderers' Guild
Gunnersbury Park Museum
Kensington Palace, State
  Apartments & Royal
  Ceremonial Dress Collection
Museum of London
Victoria & Albert Museum

Craft
Crafts Council
Little Holland House
Victoria & Albert Museum
William Morris Gallery
William Morris Society

Decorative Art
Alfred Dunhill Collection
Clockmakers' Company
  Collection
Courtauld Institute Galleries
Diocesan Treasury in the Crypt
  of St Paul's Cathedral
Fan Museum
Fenton House
Forty Hall Museum
Geffrye Museum
Harrow Museum & Heritage
  Centre
Jewish Museum
Library & Museum of the United
  Grand Lodge of England
Museum of London
Percival David Foundation of
  Chinese Art
Pitshanger Manor Museum
Riesco Collection of Chinese
  Ceramics
Sir John Soane's Museum
Victoria & Albert Museum
Wallace Collection
William Morris Gallery

Design
British Architectural Library
  Drawings Collection and RIBA
  Heinz Gallery
Brooking Collection
Design Museum
Little Holland House
Silver Studio Collection
Victoria & Albert Museum
William Morris Gallery
William Morris Society

Film & Photography
Barbican Art Gallery
British Council Collection
Bruce Castle Museum
Imperial War Museum
Island History Trust
Kingston-upon-Thames
  Museum & Heritage Centre
London Transport Museum
Museum of London

Museum of the Moving Image
Victoria & Albert Museum
Wimbledon Society Museum

Furniture
Forty Hall Museum
Geffrye Museum
Iveagh Bequest, Kenwood
Osterley Park House
Syon House
Victoria & Albert Museum
Wallace Collection

Geology
Bexley Museum
Bromley Museum
Cuming Museum
Greenwich Borough Museum
Harrow School Old Speech
  Room Gallery
Horniman Museum
Natural History Museum
University College Department
  of Geological Sciences

Historic Buildings
Bexley Museum
Boston Manor House
Brooking Collection
Bromley Museum
Bruce Castle Museum
Brunel's Engine House
Carlyle's House
Carshalton Water Tower
Chiswick House
Church Farm House Museum
Dulwich Picture Gallery
Epping Forest Museum & Queen
  Elizabeth's Hunting Lodge
Forty Hall Museum
Gunnersbury Park Museum
Ham House
Hampton Court Palace
Harrow Museum & Heritage
  Centre
Heritage Centre, Honeywood
HM Tower of London
Iveagh Bequest, Kenwood

Museums by subject

Keats House
Kensington Palace, State
  Apartments & Royal
  Ceremonial Dress Collection
Kew Palace and Queen
  Charlotte's Cottage
Leighton House Museum
Linley Sambourne House
Little Holland House
Marble Hill House
Museum of Fulham Palace
Museum of the Order of St John
Orleans House Gallery
Osterley Park House
Pitshanger Manor Museum
Prince Henry's Room
Queen's House
Rangers House
St Bride's Crypt Museum
Sutton House
Syon House
Tower Bridge
Upminster Tithe Barn
Upminster Windmill
Valence House Museum
Vestry House Museum
Whitehall, Cheam
Wimbledon Windmill Museum

Maps & Globes
Barnet Museum
British Museum
National Maritime Museum
Science Museum
Valence House Museum
Wimbledon Society Museum

Medical Science
Bethlem Royal Hospital Archives
  & Museum
British Dental Association
  Museum
British Optical Association
  Foundation Collection
British Oxygen Company
  Museum (Charles King
  Collection)

Centre for Medical Science and
  History and Wellcome Institute
  for the History of Medicine
  (Fourth Floor Exhibition)
Florence Nightingale Museum
Freud Museum
Gordon Museum
Hospital for Sick Children
Hunterian Museum
Institute of Ophthalmology
London Chest Hospital
Michael Faraday's Laboratory &
  Museum
Museum of the Order of St John
Museum of the Royal
  Pharmaceutical Society of
  Great Britain
National Army Museum
Odontological Museum
Old Operating Theatre, Museum
  & Herb Garret
Royal College of Obstetricians
Royal College of Physicians
Royal Hospital Chelsea
Royal London Hospital Museum
  & Archives Centre
St Bartholomew's Hospital
  Anaesthetics Museum
St Bartholomew's Hospital
  Pathology Museum
St Bernard's Hospital Museum
Science Museum
Springfield Hospital Museum
Wellcome Museum of Anatomy
Wellcome Museum of
  Pathology

Military History
Apsley House
Cabinet War Rooms
Guards Museum
HM Tower of London
HMS Belfast
Imperial War Museum
Inns of Court & City Yeomanry
  Museum
London Irish Rifles
London Scottish Regimental
  Museum

Museum of Artillery in the
  Rotunda
Museum of the Honourable
  Artillery Company
Polish Institute & Sikorski
  Museum
Royal Air Force Museum
Royal Armouries
Royal Artillery Regimental
  Museum
Royal Fusiliers Museum
Royal Hospital Chelsea
Royal Military School of Music
Westminster Dragoons Museum

Multicultural
Black Cultural Archives/Museum
British Museum
Commonwealth Institute
Cuming Museum
Design Museum
Grange Museum of Community
  History
Hackney Museum
Horniman Museum
Museum of Mankind
Oriental and India Office
  Collections
Polish Institute & Sikorski
  Museum
Royal Armouries
Victoria & Albert Museum

Natural History
Bayhurst Wood Country Park
Bexley Museum
Charles Darwin Memorial
  Museum
Chelsea Physic Garden
Croydon Natural History &
  Scientific Society
Cuming Museum
East Ham Nature Reserve
Epping Forest Museum & Queen
  Elizabeth's Hunting Lodge
Greenwich Borough Museum
Harrow School Old Speech
  Room Gallery
Horniman Museum

Kew Collections of Economic
Botany
Museum of Garden History
Museum of Zoology &
Comparative Anatomy
Natural History Museum
Passmore Edwards Museum
Pumphouse Educational
Museum

Paintings & Watercolours
Arts Council Collection
Bankside Gallery
Barbican Art Gallery
Ben Uri Art Society
Bethlem Royal Hospital Archives
& Museum
British Architectural Library
Drawings Collection & RIBA
Heinz Gallery
British Council Collection
British Museum
Courtauld Institute Galleries
Dulwich Picture Gallery
Fan Museum
Forty Hall Museum
Government Art Collection
Guildhall Art Gallery
Hampstead Museum
Harrow School Old Speech
Room Gallery
Imperial War Museum
Iveagh Bequest, Kenwood
Kew Gardens Gallery
Leighton House Museum
Marble Hill House
Marianne North Gallery
National Army Museum
National Gallery
National Portrait Gallery
Oriental and India Office
Collections
Orleans House Gallery
Queen's Gallery
Rangers House
Royal Academy of Arts
Royal College of Music
Department of Portraits
Royal College of Physicians
Saatchi Collection

St Bartholomew's Hospital
Archives
Sir John Soane's Museum
South London Gallery
Syon House
Tate Gallery
Thomas Coram Foundation for
Children
University College Art Collection
Valence House Museum
Victoria & Albert Museum
Wallace Collection
William Morris Gallery
William Morris Society
Wimbledon Society Museum

**Performing Arts & Sound
Archives**
British Museum
Fenton House
Horniman Museum
Museum of the Moving Image
Musical Museum
Normansfield Hospital Theatre
Puppet Centre Trust
Rangers House
Royal Ballet School Archive
Royal College of Music
Department of Portraits
Royal College of Music Museum
of Instruments
Royal Military School of Music
Royal Opera House Archives
Shakespeare Globe Museum
Theatre Museum
Victoria & Albert Museum
Vintage Wireless Museum

Period Rooms
Barnet Museum
Cabinet War Rooms
Carlyle's House
Charles Darwin Memorial
Museum
Church Farm House Museum
Courtauld Institute Galleries
Cutty Sark the Clipper Ship
Dickens House Museum
Dr Johnson's House

Erith Museum
Freud Museum
Geffrye Museum
Grange Museum of Community
History
HMS Belfast
Imperial War Museum
Keats House
Kensington Palace, State
Apartments & Royal
Ceremonial Dress Collection
Leighton House Museum
Linley Sambourne House
London Fire Brigade Museum
Museum of London
Pitshanger Manor Museum
Ragged School Museum
Valence House Museum
Vestry House Museum
Whitehall, Cheam
William Morris Gallery

Personalia
Apsley House (Wellington)
Baden Powell House
Brunel's Engine House
Cabinet War Rooms (Churchill)
Carlyle's House
Charles Darwin Memorial
Museum
Dickens House Museum
Dr Johnson's House
Florence Nightingale Museum
Freud Museum
Keats House
Leighton House Museum
Linley Sambourne House
Little Holland House (Dickenson)
Michael Faraday's Laboratory &
Museum
National Portrait Gallery
Prince Henry's Room (Pepys)
Sherlock Holmes Museum
Sir John Soane's Museum
Wesley's Chapel and House
Westminster Abbey Museum
(Royal effigies)
William Morris Gallery
William Morris Society

Museums by subject

Postal History
British Museum
Bruce Castle Museum
National Postal Museum

Prints & Drawings
Barbican Art Gallery
Ben Uri Art Society
Bethlem Royal Hospital Archives
& Museum
British Architectural Library
Drawings Collection & RIBA
Heinz Gallery
British Museum
Courtauld Institute Galleries
Dulwich Picture Gallery
Guildhall Art Gallery
Guildhall Library (Print Room)
Hogarth's House
Museum of London
Oriental and India Office
Collections
Orleans House
Sir John Soane's Museum
Tate Gallery
University College Art Collection
Victoria & Albert Museum
Wallace Collection
Wimbledon Society Museum

Public Services
Kew Bridge Steam Museum
London Fire Brigade Museum
London Gas Museum
London Transport Museum
Metropolitan Police Thames
Division Museum
Metropolitan Police Traffic
Museum
National Postal Museum
Public Record Office Museum
Story of Telecommunications
see also Medical Science

Religion
All Hallows by the Tower
Undercroft Museum
British Museum

Czech Memorial Scrolls Centre
Diocesan Treasury in the Crypt
of St Paul's Cathedral
Jewish Museum
London Museum of Jewish Life
Museum of Fulham Palace
St Bride's Crypt Exhibition
Salvation Army International
Heritage Centre
Wesley's Chapel and House
(incorporating the Museum of
Methodism)
Westminster Abbey Museum

Science & Technology
Brunel's Engine House
Carshalton Water Tower
Kew Bridge Steam Museum
Kirkaldy Testing Museum
Michael Faraday's Laboratory
and Museum (Royal Institution)
Old Royal Observatory
Science Museum
Story of Telecommunications
Tower Bridge

Sculpture
Arts Council Collection
Ben Uri Art Society
British Council Collection
British Museum
Courtauld Institute Galleries
Sir John Soane's Museum
Tate Gallery
Victoria & Albert Museum
Wallace Collection

Ships & Maritime History
All Hallows by the Tower
Undercroft Museum
Cutty Sark the Clipper Ship
HMS Belfast
London Canal Museum
National Maritime Museum
Old Royal Observatory
Science Museum
Tower Bridge
Tower Hill Pageant

Social History
Amalgamated Engineering and
Electrical Union Collection
Barnet Museum
Bethlem Royal Hospital Museum
& Archives
Bexley Museum
Black Cultural Archives/Museum
Bramah Tea and Coffee
Museum
Bromley Museum
Bruce Castle Museum
Chartered Insurance Institute
Museum
Church Farm House Museum
Crystal Palace Museum
Cuming Museum
Czech Memorial Scrolls Centre
Erith Museum
Grange Museum of Community
History
Greenwich Borough Museum
Gunnersbury Park Museum
Hackney Museum
Hampstead Museum
Harrow Museum & Heritage
Centre
Island History Trust
Kew Bridge Steam Museum
Kingston-upon-Thames
Museum & Heritage Centre
Livesey Museum
London Canal Museum
London Fire Brigade Museum
London Gas Museum
London Museum of Jewish Life
Museum of Fulham Palace
Museum of Garden History
Museum of London
Museum of Richmond
Museum on the Move
Passmore Edwards Museum
Public Record Office Museum
Ragged School Museum
Royal London Hospital Museum
& Archives Centre
St Bride's Crypt Exhibition
Upminster Tithe Barn
Valence House Museum
Vestry House Museum
Wandle Industrial Museum

Wandsworth Museum
Wimbledon Society Museum
Wimbledon Windmill Museum

Societies & Organisations
Amalgamated Engineering and
Electrical Union Collection
Baden Powell House
British Optical Association
Foundation Collection
Chartered Insurance Institute
Museum
Clockmakers' Company
Collection
Embroiderers' Guild
Library & Museum of the United
Grand Lodge of England
MCC Museum
Museum of the Order of St John

Ragged School Museum
Trades Union Congress
Collection
Wimbledon Lawn Tennis
Museum

Sporting History
Baden Powell House
Bethnal Green Museum of
Childhood
British Museum
Design Museum
Hampton Court Palace
Horniman Museum
Island History Trust
MCC Museum
Museum of London
Royal Armouries
Rugby Museum

Wimbledon Lawn Tennis
Museum

Toys & Games
Bethnal Green Museum of
Childhood
London Toy & Model Museum
Pollock's Toy Museum
Puppet Centre Trust

Transport
Gunnersbury Park Museum
London Canal Museum
London Transport Museum
Metropolitan Police Traffic
Museum
North Woolwich Old Station
Museum
Science Museum

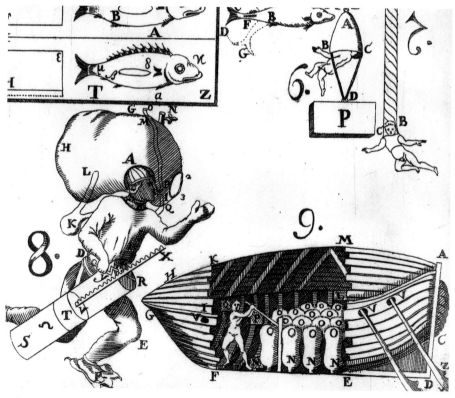

Wellcome Institute for the History of Medicine

Museum of London

Exhibition & Heritage Venues

Age Exchange Reminiscence
  Centre
11 Blackheath Village
London SE3 9LA
☎ 081-318 9105

The Banqueting House
Whitehall
London SW1A 2ER
☎ 071-930 4179

Battersea Arts Centre
Old Town Hall
Lavender Hill
London SW11 5TF
☎ 071-223 2223

Business Design Centre
52 Upper Street
Islington Green
London N1 0QH
☎ 071-359 3535

Camden Arts Centre
Arkwright Road
London NW3 6DG
☎ 071-435 2643
☎ 071-435 5224

Canada House Gallery
Canada House
Trafalgar Square
London SW1Y 5BJ
☎ 071-629 9492

Contemporary Applied Arts
43 Earlham Street
London WC2H 9LD
☎ 071-836 6993

Design Council
28 Haymarket
London SW1Y 4SU
☎ 071-839 8000

Gipsy Moth IV
King William Walk
Greenwich
London SE10 9HT
☎ 081-858 3445

Goethe Institute London
50 Princes Gate
Exhibition Road
London SW7 2PH
☎ 071-411 3400

Hayward Gallery
Belvedere Road
London SE1 8XX
☎ 071-928 3144
☎ 071-261 0127

Institute of Contemporary Arts
Nash House
The Mall
London SW1Y 5BD
☎ 071-930 6393

Kathleen & May
St Mary Overy Dock
Cathedral Street
Southwark
London SE1 9DE
☎ 071-403 3965
☎ 071-858 2698

Lauderdale House
Waterlow Park
Highgate Hill
London N6
☎ 081-348 8716

The Mall Galleries
The Mall
London SW1
☎ 071-930 6844

Museum of Installation
33 Great Sutton Street
London EC1V ODX
☎ 071-253 0802
☎ 071-582 1588

Old Palace, Croydon
Old Palace Road
Croydon
Surrey
☎ 081-680 5877

Photographers' Gallery
5/8 Great Newport Street
London WC2H 7HY
☎ 071-831-1772

Royal College of Art Gallery
Kensington Gore
London SW7 2EU
☎ 071-584 5020

Serpentine Gallery
Kensington Gardens
London W2 3XA
☎ 071-402 6075

Southside House
Wimbledon Common
London SW19 4RJ
☎ 081-946 7643
☎ 081-947 2491

Streatham Society Collection
142 Harborough Road
Streatham
London SW16 2XW
☎ 081-677 2537

Thames Barrier Visitor Centre
Unity Way
Woolwich
London SE18 5NJ
☎ 081-854 1373

Whitechapel Art Gallery
80-82 Whitechapel High Street
London E1 7QX
☎ 071-377 0107
☎ 071-377 5015

Archives & Libraries

Ashmole Archive
Department of Classics
King's College London
Strand
London WC2R 2LS
☎ 071-873 2343

Book Trust
Book House
45 East Hill
London SW18 2QZ
☎ 081-870 9055

British Library
Humanities & Social Sciences
Great Russell Street
London WC1B 3DG
☎ 071-636 1544

British Olympic Library
1 Wandsworth Plain
London SW18 1EH
☎ 081-871 2677

Fawcett Library
London Guildhall University
Old Castle Street
London E1 7NT
☎ 071-247 5826
☎ 071-320 1189

Hammersmith & Fulham
Archives and Local History
Centre
The Lilla Huset
191 Talgarth Road
London W6 8BJ
☎ 081-741 5159
☎ 081-748 3020 x3850

Kennel Club Library
Kennel Club
1-5 Clarges Street
Piccadilly
London W1Y 8AB
☎ 071-499 0844

Lambeth Palace Library
Lambeth Palace Road
London SE1 7JU
☎ 071-928 6222

Lewisham Local History Centre
Manor House
Old Road
Lee
London SE13 5SY
☎ 081-852 5050

Marx Memorial Library
37a Clerkenwell Green
London EC1R 0DU
☎ 071-253 1485

National Film Archive
21 Stephen Street
London W1P 1PL
☎ 071-255 1444

National Monuments Record
Fortress House
23 Savile Row
London W1X 2JQ
☎ 071-973 3091

National Sound Archive
(British Library)
29 Exhibition Road
London SW7 2AS
☎ 071-589 6603

Useful addresses

NSPCC Archive
67 Saffron Hill
London EC1N 8RS
☎ 071-242 1626 ext 3236

Sainsbury's Archives
J Sainsbury plc
Stamford House
Stamford Street
London SE1 9LL
☎ 071-921 6510

Science Museum Library
Imperial College Road
London SW7 5NH
☎ 071-938 8234

City Livery Companies
Apothecaries Hall
Blackfriars Lane
London EC4V 6EJ
☎ 071-236 1189

Armourers & Brasiers Hall
81 Coleman Street
London EC2R 5BJ
☎ 071-606 1199

Clothworkers Hall
Dunster Court
Mincing Lane
London EC3R 7AH
☎ 071-623 7041

Drapers Hall
Throgmorton Avenue
London EC2N 2DQ
☎ 071-588 5001

Fishmongers Hall
London Bridge
London EC4R 9EL
☎ 071-626 3531

Goldsmiths Hall
Foster Lane
London EC2V 6BN
☎ 071-606 7010

Haberdashers Hall
Staining Lane
London EC2V 4TE
☎ 071-606 0967

Ironmongers Hall
Shaftsbury Place
London EC2Y 8AA
☎ 071-606 2725

Mercers Hall
Ironmonger Lane
London EC2V 8HE
☎ 071-726 4991

Merchant Taylors Hall
30 Threadneedle Street
London EC2Y 8AY
☎ 071-588 7606

Painter-Stainers Hall
9 Little Trinity Lane
London EC4V 2AD
☎ 071-236 6258

Pewterers Hall
Oat Lane
London EC2V 7DE
☎ 071-606 9363

**Related & Professional
Bodies**
Association of Independent
  Museums
c/o Andrew Patterson
Hotties Science and Arts Centre
PO Box 68
Chalon Way
St Helens
Merseyside WA9 1LL
☎ 0744-21515

Architectural Association
  School of Architecture
34-36 Bedford Square
London WC1B 3ES
☎ 071-636 0974

Association for Business
  Sponsorship of the Arts
Nutmeg House
60 Gainsford Street
Butler's Wharf
London SE1 2NY
☎ 071-378 8143

British Association of Friends of
  Museums
548 Wilbraham Road
Manchester M21 1LB
☎ 061-242 3216

British Council
10 Spring Gardens
London SW1A 2BN
☎ 071-930 8466

British Tourist Authority
Head Office
Thames Tower
Black's Road
London W6 9EL
☎ 081-846 9000

Contemporary Art Society
20 John Islip Street
London SW1P 4LL
☎ 071-821 5323

Council for British Archaeology
112 Kennington Road
London SE11 6RE
☎ 071-582 0494

Department of National
  Heritage
2-4 Cockspur Street
London SW1Y 5BQ

English Heritage
(Historic Buildings &
  Monuments Commission)
Fortress House
Savile Row
London W1X 1AB
☎ 071-973 3000

English Tourist Board
Thames Tower
Black's Road
London W6 9EL
☎ 081-846 9000

Ephemera Society
12 Fitzroy Square
London W1P 5HQ
☎ 071-387 7723

International Council of
  Museums (ICOM)
Maison de l'Unesco
1 rue Miollis
75732 Paris
Cedex 15
France
☎ 47-34-05-00

Library Association
7 Ridgmount Street
London WC1E 7AE
☎ 071-636 7543

London Arts Board
Elme House
133 Long Acre
Covent Garden
London WC2E 9AF
☎ 071-240 1313

London Boroughs Grants Unit
5th Floor, Regal House
London Road
Twickenham TW1 3QS
☎ 081-891 5021

London Tourist Board and
  Convention Bureau
26 Grosvenor Gardens
Victoria
London SW1W ODU
☎ 071-730 3450
☎ 071-730 3488

London Voluntary Service
  Council
68 Chalton Street
London NW1 1JR
☎ 071-388 0241

Commonwealth Institute

Museums and Galleries
  Disability Association
  (MAGDA)
c/o The Secretary,
Kathy Niblett
City Museum and Art Gallery
Stoke-on-Trent ST1 3DW
☎ 0782-202173

Museums Association
42 Clerkenwell Close
London EC1R OPA
☎ 071-608 2933

Museum Documentation
  Association
Lincoln House
347 Cherry Hinton Road
Cambridge CB1 4DH
☎ 0223-242848

Museums & Galleries
  Commission
16 Queen Anne's Gate
London SW1H 9AA
☎ 071-233 4200

Museum Training Institute
Kershaw House
55 Well Street
Bradford BD1 5PS
☎ 0274-391056/087/092

National Art Collections Fund
20 John Islip Street
London SW1P 4JX
☎ 071-821 0404

National Campaign for the Arts
Francis House
Francis Street
London SW1P 1DE
☎ 071-828 4448